Land, People, and History

Land, People, and History

by

ELIZABETH S. HELFMAN

DAVID McKAY COMPANY, INC.

NEW YORK

1962

For
Harry

Acknowledgments

Many people have helped with the research for this book. It would be impossible to name them all. Among them are my good friends who clipped articles for me from newspapers and magazines, those who suggested just the right book, those who arranged field trips, and those who passed judgment on sentences, paragraphs, and parts of chapters, here and there.

Special thanks are due, however, to the following people who read substantial parts of the manuscript and made helpful suggestions:

Mr. Devereux Butcher, editor of *National Wildlands News;* Mr. Robert Clancy, director of the Henry George School of Social Science; Mr. Adrian C. Fox, Educational Relations Branch, Soil Conservation Service; and Dr. Paul B. Sears, Chairman of the Conservation Program, Yale University.

If any errors remain in the text, they are entirely the responsibility of the author.

Grateful acknowledgment is also made to the following publishers who gave permission for the use of copyrighted material:

American Heritage Publishing Co., for the quotation on page 211, from an article entitled "These Lands Are Ours," by Alvin M. Josephy, Jr., in *American Heritage Magazine* for August, 1961.

Beacon Press, for the quotation on page 15, from *We Sing of Life*, copyright 1955 by The American Ethical Union.

Mr. Howard Box, leader of the Brooklyn Society for Ethical Culture, for permission to quote his invocation on page 16.

Thomas Y. Crowell, for the quotation on page 121, from "Then As Each April Smiles," by Ben H. Smith.

Doubleday and Co., for the quotations on pages 176–177, from *India's Walking Saint*, by Hallam Tennyson.

Harcourt, Brace & World, Inc., for the quotation on page 94, from *Land of the Free*, copyright 1938 by Archibald MacLeish. Also for the quotations on pages 78–79, from *Complete Poems*, by Carl Sandburg.

Harper and Brothers for the quotations on pages 81–82, and 135, from *Giants in the Earth*, by O. E. Rölvaag.

Brandt & Brandt, and Holt, Rinehart & Winston, for the quotation on page 76, from *Western Star*, by Stephen Vincent Benét.

Houghton Mifflin Company, for the quotation on page 78, from *My Antonia*, by Willa Cather.

McGraw-Hill Book Company, for the quotation on pages 103–104, from *Rich Land, Poor Land*, by Stuart Chase.

David McKay Company, Inc. and Scholastic Book Services, for the quotation on page 36, from *Messenger to the Pharaoh*, by DeWolfe Morgan, subsequently published as a paper back, entitled *Great Pyramid Mystery*, by the Teen Age Book Club, Scholastic.

Oxford University Press, Inc., for the quotation on page 234, from *A Sand County Almanac and Sketches Here and There*, by Aldo Leopold.

George Ronald, for the quotation on page 166, from

Kabongo, by Richard St. Barbe Baker, with permission of George Ronald, Publisher, London.

Roosevelt University, Labor Education Division, for the quotation on page 85, from *Songs of Work and Freedom*, edited by Edith Fowke and Joe Glazer.

U.S. Department of Agriculture, for the quotation on page 101, from the film script of *The Plow That Broke the Plains*, by Pare Lorentz.

The Viking Press, for the quotations on pages 247–248, from *An Episode of Sparrows*, by Rumer Godden, copyright 1955 by Rumer Godden.

Except where otherwise indicated, photographs are from the Soil Conservation Service, United States Department of Agriculture.

Contents

Illustrations

Land, People, and History

1: This Is Our Earth

Pick up a handful of earth. Perhaps you live in the city and there is no outdoor earth you can pick up. Take a little from a flower pot. Hold it in your hand and look.

You are holding a handful of crumbled particles of rock with bits of decaying matter in it. This is soil, one of the most ordinary things in the world. Most of the surface of our earth has a layer of soil. The bottom of the ocean is lined with it.

This is the living part of the earth. All of us depend on it for our lives. Beneath this layer of soil our planet is a rocky mass as lifeless as the moon.

Perhaps we should not think of this handful of earth as being so ordinary after all. Without it, no plants could grow. Without plants, no animals could live. No people.

How can this dead-looking brown substance do all this? In the first place, soil is far from dead. It is three kinds of things: animal, vegetable, mineral. The mineral part is particles of rock, broken off and worn off the rocks of the earth by wind and water, glaciers, weather, and the complicated wear and tear of time. The larger particles are sand. Particles a little finer than sand are called silt. The finest particles are clay.

This mineral part of the soil is not the living part. Humus, the animal and vegetable matter in the soil, contains the living part. Humus is called organic matter, because it is made up of the remains of all sorts of animals (organisms) and plants, in a process of decay.

The word decay does not suggest life, but the decay of these dead plants and animals helps to make possible the life of the soil. Through decay these dead things are taken apart. Then they can be used for the growth of plants in the soil. The death of living things, through their decay, brings life to new things. Thus life on earth continues.

The decay in the soil is carried on through the action of hordes of small living creatures. Without these creatures the soil would be nothing but bits of lifeless rock and debris.

These tiny creatures belong to both the animal and vegetable kingdoms. The largest number of them is bacteria and fungi (such as moulds). Billions and billions of these live in the soil, together with a variety of tiny algae, insects, worms, and protozoa (microscopic animals). All these creatures depend on one another, through a most complicated system of relationships.

In a thimbleful of soil there may be two billion bacteria, about thirty million bits of fungi, and one hundred protozoa. They are a lovely sight under the microscope, colorful, odd-shaped, some of them whiskery.

Bacteria and fungi act on the dead matter in the soil, causing decay. In the process, certain chemicals are changed into a form which plants can use as food. Without them no plants could grow. And without the complex ability of each green leaf to manufacture its own food from materials in air and water, we could not live.

Soil is not a solid mass. Between its particles are air and water, both of which are needed for the life of the soil.

There is topsoil and subsoil. Topsoil, as the word suggests, is the top layer of soil. It is the fertile part, with the larger amount of organic matter. Most plants depend on topsoil for their growth. It is seldom deeper than the depth of a spade, anywhere in the world.

Underneath the topsoil is subsoil, about two or three feet deep. Subsoil is in the process of being made into topsoil. It consists mostly of mineral particles, with only a little organic matter. Subsoil becomes topsoil very slowly, over hundreds of years.

Under the subsoil is the rock from which came the beginnings of this soil.

These three layers are what scientists call the profile of the soil. The kind of soil it is depends on what is in each of these three layers.

There is good soil and poor soil. Good soil has a plentiful supply of the minerals plants need for their growth. It has, too, an abundance of organic matter.

Good soil can become poor worn-out soil if too many of the minerals the plants need for growth are used up. This happens when the same plants are grown on the soil, over and over again. It can become poor soil, too, when the organic matter is not continually being replaced. Man himself can bring this about.

Soil is an important part of the whole complex pattern of life on this planet. Everything that lives on earth depends on other living things, both plants and animals—in the last analysis, on the soil. In our modern world, we may depend on soil quite far from where we live. The wheat in our bread may have been grown in the soil of Kansas, our potatoes in the soil in Maine, Idaho, or Long Island, our coffee in soil in Brazil.

The science of the relationship between living organisms

and their surroundings is called ecology. You will find this science cropping up here and there throughout this book. You may recognize it even when it is not mentioned by name.

From the most minute organism to man himself, we all live together on this earth. All forms of life must take in nourishment. All forms of life multiply. If nothing stopped this multiplying of life, the earth would be overrun with some species. Take one small example. The beneficial bacteria in the soil, if they multiplied without anything to stop them, would become so numerous that they would destroy everything else, just by living. The offspring from a single one of these bacteria can multiply to seventeen million in twenty-four hours. And there are already billions in the soil.

Nature takes care of this problem. All sorts of organisms use plants and other organisms to keep themselves alive. Human beings eat plants and animals. Animals eat other animals and plants. Some creatures die of starvation or of severe weather. There is a constant struggle to survive. There are species of plants and animals which have not survived. They have made way for others which are better adapted to their surroundings. The dinosaur is the most obvious example.

From the earth, then, each living being receives what it needs to keep alive. Countless generations of plants and animals have used the same earth for their nourishment, over and over again. When they have died they have returned to the earth, to decay and enrich it. Nature has managed the balance between life and decay in a most expert fashion. There is no time when living beings do not find nourishment in the natural earth.

There have been times, however, when man has upset the balance of nature, with results which have been disastrous for himself and for other creatures. Often he has done this in his use of the land. You will find much about this in this book. .

Less than one-eighth of the land on our planet is covered with topsoil that can be used for growing food. It is on this one-eighth that most of us live.

That, with the deserts and mountain peaks, and the frozen places which we cannot use for growing food, is our land.

People have loved this land. The earth beneath our feet symbolizes for us the place where we belong, our home, our country, sometimes the whole world.

In the Psalms of the Old Testament we read of man's gratitude to his God for the earth: "Thou visitest the earth, and waterest it. . . . Thou crownest the year with thy goodness; . . . and the little hills rejoice on every side. The pastures are clothed with flocks; the valleys also are covered over with corn; they shout for joy, they also sing." (Corn here means any grain.)

And the Greek playwright Euripides in ancient times wrote:

". . . Earth, the ancient life-giver, increaseth
Joy among the meadows, like a tree."

Homesick Czech soldiers sang of the wide green fields at home when they were away at the wars.

The English earth, for Shakespeare, was "This blessed plot, this earth, this realm, this England."

This is the earth to which the people cling who live on the sides of Mount Vesuvius in Italy. They know that this is an active volcano which may someday again erupt and pour lava over their homes, down all the mountainside, but they stay.

It has been said that most Americans have not learned to love the land. This may be true. We have taken our land for granted. We have used it carelessly. But there have been those who loved our American earth. Walt Whitman was one of these. He wrote:

"Give me juicy autumnal fruit ripe and red from the orchard,
Give me a field where the unmow'd grass grows,
Give me an arbor, give me the trellis'd grape,
Give me fresh corn and wheat, give me serene-moving animals teaching content,
Give me nights perfectly quiet as on high plateaus west of the Mississippi, and I looking up at the stars. . . ."

Man has used the land in many different ways, everywhere in the world. He has used the soil well and he has brought ruin to it, since history began. It has taken people a long time to learn the importance of the care of the soil in the history of the world. Franklin D. Roosevelt, when he was President of the United States, pointed this out. He said, "The history of every nation is eventually written in the way in which it cares for its soil."

That is what this book is about.

2: Ceremonies on the Land

Early man cared a great deal about the earth beneath his feet. He could not explain it scientifically, but he could feel the life in it. And he could feel, also without explaining, his own part in this life.

Many early people believed that in the beginning there was only water in the world. Earth was made of mud or clay fished up out of the primeval waters by the spirit who created the world.

To early people, this world seemed to be ruled by spirits. Earth was the great mother who gave life to all her children. The people worshipped her. They gave her gifts because they must hurt her when they dug into the earth with their sticks or their plows.

Early people watched the changing seasons. Those who lived where the winters were cold saw the plants grow green in the spring, ripen in the summer and fall, and then seem to die as winter came. Every year this happened, and every year it was new and terrible. Early man could feel this happening also in himself. He did not even have the comfort of knowing that spring would surely come again. He must do his best to please the spirits who ruled the earth. He must give part of whatever he had to the Earth Mother. Then perhaps spring would come again. And when it did come, he would celebrate with wild dances of rejoicing.

Ancient people, too, at a much later time than early man, celebrated the rhythm of the seasons, the mystery of planting and harvest, with dance and ritual. They brought offerings to the gods of the earth. There might not be a good harvest, they thought, if people did not do the right things in their ceremonies and in their daily lives.

These ancient people believed that spirits, or gods, controlled everything that grew. Each plant grew only because some spirit wanted it to grow. Each animal had its own spirit, and so did the earth itself. Men felt that they must not only please these spirits but they must become a part of the magic that would make the rain fall on the good earth and the grain grow in it.

These were civilized people. They knew much more about the world around them than early man had ever known. But they believed in their magic because they were sure it worked. When they danced in their magic ceremonies, they, too, seemed to come alive and grow. And when the earth seemed to die in the fall, something in them died, too. They knew that man was a part of nature because they felt this in themselves.

All over the world in ancient times, often among people who had no contact with one another at all, very similar beliefs arose. In the earliest societies, the earth spirit was usually a woman, because it is women who bring forth life. The Earth Mother was worshipped everywhere.

For the ancient Greeks, Demeter was the goddess of all the cultivated earth. Her story had come to the Greeks in tales told long before by travelers from Asia, when the Greeks first gave up being wandering hunters and settled down to grow grain in their own fields. Demeter was a goddess of peace, bringing life to man.

The old Greek story tells us that Demeter's beautiful daughter, Persephone, was stolen by Pluto, god of the Underworld, and taken down to his shadowy kingdom. Demeter was inconsolable. In her anger, she refused to let any seed grow in the earth as long as her daughter was in the Underworld. There was no seedtime and harvest. People on earth were starving. No creatures could live on a barren earth. At last Zeus, the father of the gods, forced Pluto to give up Persephone for eight months of the year. During the other four months, she must live with Pluto.

While Persephone was on earth, fruit grew heavy on trees and vines, grain ripened, flowers blossomed in the meadows. When she must go again to the Underworld, every year, all things stopped growing and seemed to die. It was winter. The seeds of grain waited quietly in the earth. They would sprout in the spring, when Persephone returned.

In the Greek city of Eleusis, rites and ceremonies were held each year in honor of Demeter. In the fields where grain was harvested, part of the yield was offered to her. Women in white robes brought garlands of wheat to the altar in her honor. It was important to please Demeter so that never again would she take away the grain and the fruits of the earth.

The Roman name for Demeter was Ceres, and from this comes our word cereal. In Egypt, the Earth Mother was called Isis. In Phoenicia, she was Cybele.

Many ancient myths repeated the story of Demeter and Persephone, in different forms. Often the child of the Earth Mother was a son who became god of all growing things. This god was thought to die each year for the sake of the people and then come to life so that the grain could grow.

Like the seed, he was buried and lay quiet in the earth. Like the seed, he came to life in the spring.

In the spring, people everywhere in the ancient world held ceremonies that would ensure the growth of their seeds in the moist earth of their fields. In one such ceremony a Corn King (corn meaning any grain) drove his plow through the field while the people sang along and danced, imploring the Spring Queen (the Earth Mother) to be kind. This ceremony continued all day, until at last the Spring Queen agreed to come with flowers and lambs to bring fertility to the earth.

In the fall, or sometimes earlier in warm parts of the earth, there were harvest festivals. The Greek ceremonies in Eleusis honored Demeter. The Romans put on processions, with music and dancing and a feast, in honor of Ceres.

The crops were not to be used by the people until the ceremonies were finished. The cutting down of the grain was not a simple thing. The harvest was being taken away from the Earth Mother, and people must do what they could to make her happy in spite of this. They would offer her a part of the harvest, as a symbol for the whole of it.

In Egypt the reaper would pause after cutting the first few blades of grain, beat his breast and lament loudly, to make up for his taking of the grain.

Animals were sometimes chosen to represent the god of vegetation who must die in the fall. They would be killed as a sacrifice, then be buried or eaten. Sometimes, too, a man took the place of the god and acted out his death and his coming to life again.

In some cultures, a man, a woman, or even a child might take the place of the god and be sacrificed. There was magic in the dances and the songs of the people at harvest time.

We read in the Old Testament of the spring and harvest

festivals of the ancient Hebrews. These people did not seem to be afraid that spring would not come. "While the earth remaineth," says the Bible, "seedtime and harvest . . . shall not cease."

Passover was originally an agricultural festival, held at the beginning of the first grain harvest of the year. Its ritual still includes a prayer for dew, which was an important source of life-giving water in Palestine. But the main purpose of the festival today is to commemorate the coming of the Jews out of Egypt.

The first grain harvest came early in this warm subtropical country, so Passover is a spring festival. These words from the Song of Solomon in the Old Testament are still read in the Passover service: "For, lo, the winter is past, the rain is over and gone; the flowers appear on the earth; the time of the singing of birds is come, and the voice of the turtle [dove] is heard in our land."

A sheaf of grain, gathered just before this first harvest, was brought to the priest in the Temple. "The first of the first-fruits of thy land," says the Old Testament, "thou shalt bring into the house of the Lord thy God."

Seven weeks after the second day of Passover, in our month of June, came Shevuoth, the feast of weeks. The first harvest was finished. Pilgrims went to the Temple in Jerusalem carrying part of this first harvest, barley, wheat, grapes, and other foods of the earth.

"How blessed," they sang, "are the people to whom has been given this full harvest."

The pilgrims climbed the hill to the Temple, carrying their offerings on their shoulders in baskets, chanting, "This day have I proclaimed unto the Lord."

At home, housewives ground fresh flour from the new grain and baked bread and cakes for the family feast.

In the fall, at the time of the last harvest of the year, came Succoth, the Feast of Ingathering. This, too, was provided for in the Old Testament: "Thou shalt keep . . . the feast of ingathering, which is in the end of the year, when thou hast gathered in thy labors out of the field."

"And thou shalt rejoice in thy feast, thou, and thy son, and thy daughter, and thy manservant, and thy maidservant, and the Levite, the stranger, and the fatherless, and the widow, that are within thy gates."

This festival of thanksgiving was kept with joy for seven days. It is often called the Feast of Tabernacles or Booths, because at this time little booths (called tabernacles or succahs) were made from the branches of trees, on the roofs of houses, in courtyards, and in other places. Nehemiah gives instructions for this in the Old Testament: "Go forth unto the mount, and fetch olive branches, and pine branches, and myrtle branches, and palm branches, and branches of thick trees, to make booths."

These booths recalled the desert wandering of the Jews after they came out of Egypt. The people had lived then in rough huts. The booths also recalled those in which Jewish farmers lived during the harvest.

On each of the seven days of Succoth, pilgrims marched around the altar singing hymns and waving palm branches. There were special ceremonies for each day.

All of these Jewish festivals are still kept today, though their original meaning is not always remembered. Harvest is celebrated with gratitude by Jews in the modern state of Israel. There is an Israeli reaper's dance, hakotzrim, in which couples move as the reapers do when they cut grain. The man in each couple is the farmer; he swings his lady back and forth like a scythe. The harvest is personified.

In the Middle Ages in Europe, long after ancient times, ceremonies for seedtime and harvest continued, and there was still a feeling of magic about them. Customs varied from place to place. Harvest Home was a special time in England. Reapers and their friends and sweethearts accompanied the last load of grain with garlands of branches and flowers, singing merrily. Here is one of their songs:

> "The boughs do shake and the bells do ring,
>   So merrily comes our harvest in,
>   Our harvest in, our harvest in,
>   So merrily comes our harvest in.

> "We have plowed, and we have sowed,
>   We have reaped, and we have mowed,
>   We have brought home every load,
>   Hip, hip, hip,
>   *Harvest Home!*"

In some parts of Europe people celebrated the burial of winter in the spring. A ragged straw figure was dragged wildly through the village and buried, or executed by drowning, or hanging, or being torn apart. Gay shouts of onlookers helped the ceremony along. There would then be a play about winter's defeat. The actors would stamp hard on the sleeping earth to bring it to life. These ceremonies had their beginnings in a very ancient past.

There were dances before and after sowing to ensure a good harvest. The dancers leaped high in the air to force the seed to grow. This was explained in a song:

> "If you do not higher leap
>   When the grain comes, you will weep."

There were Morris dances and sword dances, also with leaping and stamping. Swords took the place of the victim who would have been sacrificed in earlier times.

In the Morris dances, hands were raised up as high as the grain should grow. Stamping should waken the earth. So should the jingling of bells in time with the rhythm of the dance. Evil spirits would be frightened away.

In the Morris bean-planting dance, planting sticks held by the dancers were raised and then thrust down as if to make holes in the earth to receive the seed.

This leaping and stamping in dances did not take place only in Europe. In many parts of the world, even today, dancers imitate the growth of the grain in a dance. In Borneo, high leaps are made to make the crops grow high. Rows of dancing girls wave their arms like stalks of grain in the wind.

Morris dances are still done in some parts of England to-day, and in this country. In some farming villages in Europe straw figures, or a person wrapped in a sheaf of straw, still represent the Corn Mother. But the magic is not the same.

May Day is another time of ancient magic and rejoicing in many parts of the world. Spring has really come then. The fruits of the earth are on their way, but magic may be needed to ensure a good harvest. May flowers are gathered early in the morning. The Queen of the May is crowned. Dances are still done around the maypole in England and in parts of the United States.

"Round and round the maypole,
   Merrily we go,
 Tripping, tripping lightly,
   Singing as we go."

The American Indians had their planting and harvest ceremonies, too. The Pawnees at harvest time would wind long
scarves of green leaves around their shoulders and twist
dried corn leaves into their hair, with a tassel waving above.
They would bend and sway in a dance, as the corn swayed
in the wind, back and forth across the fields.

The magic of the old ceremonies was not just nonsense.
Of course, it did not make the seeds sprout more quickly or
the harvest grow more full. But it helped man himself to feel
at ease with the world. It helped him to remember his place
in the community of living things on this earth.

We have not entirely forgotten the old ways, though most
of the magic is gone. We have our Thanksgiving feast and
are truly grateful for the harvest. We may sing:

"Give thanks for the corn and the wheat that are reaped,
   For labor well done and for barns that are heaped,
   For the sun and the dew and the sweet honey-comb,
   For the rose and the song and the harvest brought home."

Children sing:

"Oats, peas, beans and barley grow,
   Oats, peas, beans and barley grow."

This was once a song to bring good luck to the crops.

The Christmas tree long ago was a sacred tree. People
danced around it to bring back life to the sleeping forests
after the long winter. We still have our Christmas trees.

Easter is the great spring celebration of the Christian
church.

Man has grown away from the land and the spirits that
he thought used to inhabit it. But every now and then he
remembers. Every now and then a farmer feels it is some-

how his fault if, after he has followed all the rules of good farming, the harvest isn't good. There must be something else he should have done. Maybe he didn't live right, and this is his punishment. Maybe he can do better next year. Not just the earth and the rain can do better, but the farmer, too, and whatever spirits out of the past may be there to help him.

We can feel a part of the community of growing things as we hear this present-day invocation for a religious service:

"As in every land beneath the sun men have gathered since their age began, so do we also gather amidst the pageantry of earth and sky.

"Like them we watch the scroll of the seasons that unwinds before us—the warm and the cold, the rain and the clear, the time of growth and the time of rest, and the recurring parable of seedtime and harvest.

"And like them, for ourselves and our children, we labor to bring forth from the earth the bread of sustenance and the wine of gladness.

"And we would join with them in mind and act that the bread might be shared amongst us and the gladness known among all of the children of men."

3: Early Man and the Land

Early man lived on the land. People live on the land now, too, but not in the same way he did. Early man built his hut, when he made one at all, directly on the earth. He slept on the ground, in his hut or in his cave, or in the open under the stars.

Early man walked on the earth with his bare feet. He felt the soft springiness of earth when he walked under the trees of the forest. He felt the hard push of it against his feet on the path where he went to the brook to drink.

Early man watched the earth. He saw rain from the sky fall on the ground and soak into it. He knew the damp smell of the earth after the rain. Sometimes he found puddles in hollow places when the earth had taken in all the water it could hold. Now and then he may have picked up a handful of earth in his rough hand, looked at it, and wondered.

But this man did not have much time for wonder. He lived in a cruel world, and he needed most of his time and all of his sharp wits just for the business of keeping alive. It was his sharp wits that made him better than the animals. Without such wits, in those wild times, no two-legged creature with so little fur, and few tools to work with, could have survived.

17

Plants grew on the earth. Fruit that was good to eat grew on the trees. Berries ripened on bushes in the warm sun. The plants that grew from the earth needed water, just as the animals did, and man himself. When it did not rain, plants could not stay green and grow. All this man knew, and he learned which fruits of the earth were good to eat. For some of his food, too, he hunted the wild animals with whom he shared the earth.

The men in those times did the hunting. It was the women who picked fruit, dug up the wild roots that were good to eat, and gathered wild plants, while they cared for the children. It was probably a woman who had a new idea when she found a bush so full of berries that she could not pick them all before dark. She pulled it out of the earth, carried it home, and dug a hole for it in the earth beside her cave. This was a kind of planting.

It was a long time before anyone knew what seeds were. People did know that many seeds were good to eat. But no one was sure that seeds in the moist earth would sprout and grow into new plants. This was a mysterious thing that could hardly be believed.

We don't know when people learned to plant seeds themselves. Probably the first time it happened was an accident. A few seeds had been spilled in soft earth outside the cave. Before long little green shoots came up. In time they grew tall like any shoots of wild plants and had their own seeds.

Perhaps one of the women had seen the seeds fall. She watched the plants growing. Then she scattered a handful of seeds in the earth beside the cave. These, too, grew.

After this, it was not hard to discover that seeds grew best in soft earth. And earth could be made soft by scratching it with a sharp stick or, later, digging with a stone hoe. This, too, was done by the women at first, with an anxious prayer to the spirit of the earth, who might be hurt by the sharp stick or the hoe.

Children had not been of much help in the wild business of hunting. But they could help with this planting and growing. They could pull weeds out of the earth around the growing plants. Even the youngest could wave their arms to scare away the birds and little animals that came to eat the seed.

Planting seeds in this way made it possible for people to grow more edible plants than they ever could find growing wild. Dried plants could be stored in caves and eaten during the cold lean days of winter. When there was enough food, people could live in their home caves all winter. There was no need to wander to far places in the winter cold, searching for something to eat.

For the first time, the earth man walked on was being made to serve him. This was the beginning of great changes in the history of people on the earth, and important changes in the soil itself. Soil that is dug and planted and harvested by man is no longer wild.

The seed scatterers were the first farmers. Planting was probably first discovered by different people, in places far apart on the earth. Once it was discovered by a few people, others would learn. Before long, whole tribes who had been just hunters and food gatherers became hunters and farmers. Then they need not always lead a wandering life, as they had before. Now they might stay for months near the fields they had planted, waiting for their crops to ripen.

These were not very expert farmers. For a long time they did not even know how to bring water to their fields when the rain did not come. But this, too, they learned.

They watched the puddles in the hollow places of the earth after the rain. Sometimes these puddles were big enough so people could scoop up water in a skin bag or a clay pot and take it to the few plants they were trying to grow beside the cave.

Then someone thought of digging a deeper hole, with his bare hands or with a sharp stone. This hole would hold still more water when the rain came. It would not keep on being full of water, like a well, but sometimes there was water for the plants for a long time after the rain. Sometimes, too, this meant water for people to drink, when the brook went dry.

Later, one man who did a little more wondering than his neighbors thought of digging ditches between his rows of plants, to hold the water when the stream beside his fields overflowed in the spring or after a heavy rain. Other farmers did the same thing. Seeds could be planted and grow in these fields when the stream was no longer in flood. Even if it did not rain.

People discovered that by working together they could dig deeper ditches and water bigger fields.

This was the first irrigation. After that, people could stay even longer in one place. In a dry year, they need not go looking for greener places.

Before he learned to grow his own crops, man did not use the earth any more than the animals did. There was a balance among all living things. Plants grew and some were eaten. Animals ate plants and one another. Dead plants and animals were returned to the earth and decayed there. Man was a part of this balance, and there were never enough people to upset it.

But when man learned to use the earth he walked on for growing food and for herding cattle, another way of life began. Digging up the earth, planting seeds and pulling weeds is not like what happens in nature. Soil can be worn out if it is used over and over again to grow the same plants. The minerals plants need for their growth can be used up. And soil is no longer good if dead plant materials do not become mixed with it and decay in it, feeding the millions of tiny organisms in the soil. The balance of nature began to be disturbed when the earth was first scratched with a sharp stick or a stone hoe.

Still, the use of the soil was not really a problem for the first farmers. There was plenty of land and there were few people. Of course, none of the land was empty, just waiting for the farmer's seeds. He had to clear away the scrub and forest that he found growing there. His stone hoes and axes could not do this job at all well. But he had learned to use fire. Often he would burn off whatever he found growing on a piece of land he wanted to use. Then he would dig up the earth as best he could, plant his seeds, and grow his crops there for a few seasons.

When the land was worn out and their crops would not grow well there any more, people would simply move on to another place. The deserted land usually grew back to scrub and forest.

The first grains that men grew in early Europe and Asia were wheat and barley. These still grow wild in western Asia. They were good food, not hard to store, and not too hard to raise. In much of the area where these grains were grown, in what is now Asia Minor and nearby places, the winters were not too cold for growing plants. Winters were rainy, summers were hot and dry. When the seeds of wheat and barley ripened in May and June, the early farmers gathered them. Then they stored the seeds (and ate some of them) through the dry months from July through September. When the first autumn rains wet the earth, the farmers planted much of the seed. Small green shoots of grain would push up out of the earth in the cool winter rain.

The earliest farmers probably did not eat most of their wheat and barley. They drank it. Before man learned to make bread, he made beer from his grain. Beer could be kept for a long time without spoiling. This beer made directly from the grain the farmers harvested was food for the people.

Early farmers had not given up hunting wild animals. Meat was good to eat as well as grain. People learned to catch fish in the rivers and eat them. They still gathered wild berries and roots in the woods. But it was the grain they grew in the fields that made the most difference in their lives. People could settle down in one place.

In what we now call Latin America, the pattern of life for the early farmers was much the same, except that their chief grain was the wild ancestor of maize.

Growing grain the way these early farmers did was good for the people. It was hard work to get the fields ready for the seed, and to plant it. But after that there was not much to do about the grain except to pull up weeds, until the harvest time in May and June. Then, nothing more until another planting. There was time to wonder about the world. Time for some of the people to draw pictures to help their magic. Time to dance and sing and make designs on clay pots. Life was changing.

Progress was slow. Life could not have been easy. It took courage to change man's ways, to plant a field with seed even if there might not be quite enough grain for food that summer, to watch it and wait for it to ripen. It was hard to believe that this time, again, the grain would grow.

Even so, farming began to develop as a way of life all over the world, wherever there were people who had learned enough about digging the earth and planting seeds. Wherever, too, people had learned to work together. This brought about such a tremendous change in the lives of men that it has been called a revolution.

Before this time, man had lived a lonely life, depending for protection only on himself and the few families who settled near him. This changed as he grew more and more grain in his fields and learned to water them. Life was centered around the fields at planting and at harvest time. Even at other times, the grain must be watched. Many families gathered with other families to help one another. Together they dug their irrigation ditches and took care of them.

Farmers claimed as their own their favorite plot of land, and land ownership began. In time, houses were built beside the fields. A group of houses became a village. People were learning to live together.

When we speak of early man, we mean people who lived many thousands of years ago, before there was any written history. No one knows exactly how long ago this was.

Agriculture, the growing of crops for food, began at least seven thousand years ago. Probably man first learned to grow grain up in the hills where the wild grain was already growing. He could be sure of enough rain in the hills.

Later, people moved down to the valleys. They may have first irrigated their fields beside small streams at the foot of mountains. There, the streams would sometimes overflow into the fields. Flooding waters would wash down rich soil from the hills.

It was in the valleys of great rivers, the Tigris and Euphrates in Asia Minor and the Nile in Africa, that civilization began. This did not just happen. Civilization could not have started at all if people had not learned how to use the rich soil in the valleys of these rivers.

4: Early Agriculture

It was not hard to learn farming in the valley of the Nile River in Egypt. The soil was rich, and no matter how much it was used, it stayed that way. This was because the river brought down silt from distant mountains and spread it out over the fields when it overflowed, every summer.

This flooding of the Nile taught irrigation to the early Egyptians, more than six thousand years ago. There was very little rain in the Nile valley. Fields were hot and dry under the summer sun until the flood of the Nile came pouring down from faraway mountains where, in that same season, there had been torrents of rain. Water from the river stayed on the fields long enough to soak deep into the ground. Then it retreated slowly, leaving a layer of rich wet earth. This was when the Egyptians plowed and planted their seeds. The grain would grow and ripen through the cooler winter months.

Canals were dug through the fields to keep the water close to the grain as it grew. But sometimes there was not enough water in the canals. In some places, too, the banks at the edge of the river were too high. Water was then lifted from the river in the buckets of a shadoof and poured onto the land or into the canals. A shadoof consists of a pole fastened between the tops of two posts. The end of the pole that is over the river has a bucket attached. The end toward the land has a lump of dried mud for a weight. The Egyptian farmer would stand in the water, pull down the bucket and fill it, and then let it go. The clay weight on the other end of the pole, heavier than the bucket, would help swing the bucket up so that water could be dumped into the canal or onto the land. The shadoof is still in use in Egypt today.

Using a shadoof all day was hard work. So was plowing and planting, weeding and harvesting. But nowhere in the world was this work so richly rewarded. In the dark earth beside the Nile, grain grew lush and tall. There was enough food for everyone, except for the few terrible times when there was drought in the faraway mountains, and the flooding of the Nile was not enough.

Even this Nile River valley had not always been so good for planting. For hundreds of years before this time, people had lived farther away from the river. For hundreds of years there had been enough rain. Slowly the climate changed; there was less and less rain. The land became a desert.

The people looked at the green valley beside the Nile River. It did not look very promising. There were no fields of grain then, no neat patterns of canals. Instead, there was a vast marshy jungle full of reeds and tall feathery papyrus plants. In the few open stretches, hippopotamuses and crocodiles lived and fought to survive. Elephants and wild boars roamed the swamps.

Wild as it was, this was the land where these people must live if they were to survive. Only such a great need could have made them struggle with it. They made war on the animals. They dug channels to drain the swamps. Banks had to be built to keep too much water from pouring over the land. Reeds and papyri were cleared out. After the people had done all this, the land was theirs. When the Egyptians gave thanks to their gods for a good harvest, they knew what it was they should be thankful for: the good earth, the river that watered it, and their own hard work which made this earth their own.

People living in this rich valley had no reason to move away. They stayed right where they were. Villages were built on the higher land near the fields, rows of houses made of mud and straw. People could grow more than just enough food for themselves. Some of the people had time for singing and dancing, time to paint pictures, to write on sheets of papyrus, to chip away at stone sculptures. Some of the people, at least, had time to wonder about the world. Others were slaves, still busy with nothing more than the grim business of keeping themselves and other people alive.

No one knows just when agriculture began in the Nile valley. Thousands of years passed before the period of time which we call ancient. This period began almost six thousand years ago and lasted for more than four thousand years, until the end of the Roman Empire.

In ancient times, great civilizations grew up in the countries bordering on, or near, the Mediterranean Sea. Early in this period the Egyptians created one of the most magnificent civilizations the world has ever known. None of this would have been possible without the River Nile and the rich earth beside it.

As you can see, the use of the land was not much of a problem to the early Egyptians. The river watered the land and renewed it, every year. For a long time, the Egyptians had no need to learn much about right and wrong ways of using the land.

Not far from Egypt, east across the Arabian peninsula in Asia Minor, are two other great rivers, the Tigris and the

Euphrates. Here, too, farming began in very early times, and a great civilization developed. We are not sure whether farming started first in the Nile valley or in the valley of the Tigris and Euphrates rivers. In both valleys, people could become civilized at such an early period of history because they lived on rich earth which grew more than enough grain for the farmer's daily needs. This rich earth would have been a useless desert without the water of the rivers.

There were important differences, however, in the way the earth was used in these two valleys.

The lower part of the valley of the Tigris and Euphrates rivers was called Sumer when history began. The people who lived there were Sumerians. Archaeologists tell us that this land was the Garden of Eden which we read about in the Bible.

Before this valley became any sort of garden, the Sumerians had to dig canals and drain the swamps. Then they cleared the land, just as the Egyptians had done in the valley of the Nile. This may have been even more of a job than it was in Egypt. Almost all the land in the valley was swampy.

The Sumerians had to work harder, too, to keep their land going after it was cleared. This, like Egypt, was a land of little rain. There were some floods along the river in the spring, when the snows melted in the mountains far to the north. A certain amount of rich earth was spread over the fields in these floods. But this was not a single dramatic life-giving event like the flooding of the Nile. More of the work had to be done by people. Deep canals had to be dug across the fields to take water to the young crops. These canals were dug farther and farther away from the rivers as more and more people came to live there.

The Babylonians, who followed the Sumerians in this valley, kept on digging canals. The water of the rivers was muddy, not just during the spring floods, but all the time. Deposits of silt settled in the canals, and little by little it clogged them up. People carried the silt out in baskets. Dozens of people, then hundreds, and finally thousands. Life itself depended on keeping the canals clear. Grain could not grow in dry earth.

Settlements grew around each system of canals; houses of mud and straw were built on the higher ground. Each town or city was responsible for its own land and water. To neglect either of these would mean starvation. So we see that the Babylonians controlled the fertility of their soil much more than the Egyptians in the valley of the Nile. They did it very well. Wide fields of grain stretched for miles beside the river. The Babylonians, like the Egyptians, stayed in their valley because they could not imagine a better place to be.

Land and water were so important to these people that Hammurabi, a Babylonian king who ruled more than a thousand years before Christ, decreed death to any person who wasted water or spoiled the land.

Nebuchadnezzar, a king of Babylonia more than a thousand years after Hammurabi, boasted: "That which no king before me had done, I did . . . great canals I dug and lined them with burnt brick laid in bitumen and brought abundant waters to all the people . . . I paved the streets of Babylon with stone from the mountains . . . magnificent palaces and temples I have built . . . Huge cedars from Mount Lebanon I cut down . . ."

Babylon, it seems, had become too rich, the people too fond of luxury. In the Old Testament we read the warnings of Hebrew prophets against the wicked city. Babylon, they warned, would become "a desolation, a dry land, and a wilderness, a land wherein no man dwelleth. . . ." "And the wild beasts . . . shall cry in their desolate houses, and dragons in their pleasant palaces."

This is just what happened, though not all at once. More and more silt washed down the rivers, from the hills to the north where too many of the cedars of Lebanon had been cut down and too many sheep and goats had stripped the hillsides. Earth washed off the unprotected hills and kept on settling in the irrigation canals of Babylonia. More and more people had to spend all their time getting this silt out of the canals. War captives were brought in to do it. Many Israelites were captured and carried away from Palestine by Nebuchadnezzar. "By the rivers of Babylon," wrote the Psalmist, "there we sat down, yea, we wept." Probably they, too, had to dig silt out of the canals and carry it off in baskets. There are still long ridges of earth in the desert, in the present-day country of Iraq, piles of this silt left there so long ago.

For hundreds of years, though, this was a prosperous land. As in Egypt, some of the people had time to be really civilized. They danced and sang. They wrote on tablets of clay made from the mud of their soil. Their sculptors worked on massive sculpture.

But the Babylonians had fewer years of peace than the Egyptians. Egypt was a land protected on both east and west by miles of waterless desert. Invaders would think twice before trying to cross such a desert. Babylonia had no such protection. Nomads swooped down from the hills, destroying and pillaging. When, as often happened, they destroyed some of the canals, there was disaster in the land. People fled. Many starved.

There were disastrous invasions, by the Assyrians to the north, the Persians, and Alexander the Great in the fourth century before Christ. At least eleven empires rose and fell there. War meant neglect of the soil, destruction or neglect of the canals on which the life of the soil depended. Each time, the canals were rebuilt. But each time it was harder; always the canals were more full of silt. The stopping up of the canals had more to do with the decline of this land than all the wars that swept over it. As time went on, fewer and fewer people lived there.

Finally, only about seven hundred years ago, the Mongols from eastern Asia poured over the land. The people were tired. They could not keep the Mongols out. These Mongols were destroyers. They ruined everything they could lay their hands on, and that included the whole intricate irrigation system. This was no longer a land where people could live. The land between the rivers went back to desert.

Much of this land is still a desert. Only a few wandering people pass over it. The rich earth remains, but no one can live on it without the deep canals to carry the water from the rivers.

You may have heard this land called Mesopotamia, which is a Greek word meaning land between two rivers. Mesopotamia was not only the southern valley of the rivers, which was Sumer and Babylonia, but the valley north of this, where the Assyrians lived.

Today, nearly seven hundred years after the Babylonian canals were destroyed by the Mongols, the government of Iraq, the present-day country between the rivers, is building dams and irrigation canals, so that the rich earth of the valley can again grow grain and people can flourish there as they did long ago.

Other river valleys were the homes of great civilizations in early times. One of these was the Indus River valley in the part of Asia that is now called West Pakistan. Here great cities grew up. Archaeologists have uncovered houses built solidly of baked bricks. Bathrooms in these houses had elaborate plumbing which drained into sewer pipes under the streets and then into the river. There were even shower baths.

Fine sculptures of stone have been uncovered in the cities of this valley. Some of the people, it seems, knew how to write, but no one today can read their writing. This limits what can be found out about the Indus civilization. What we can learn is limited, too, by the fact that this civilization was destroyed more than three thousand years ago. Historians are not even sure how it was destroyed, though perhaps this was done by less civilized invaders from the north.

The Indus civilization could not have developed without the rich soil in the valley of the river, any more than the Egyptian and Mesopotamian civilizations could have developed without the rich soil in their valleys. In the broad fields of this valley, too, the farmer planted his long rows of wheat and barley beside the canals. The earth was good to the people, year after year. Again, life was not just an endless search for enough food to keep a man alive.

The Indus River, like the Nile, the Tigris and Euphrates, brought down tons of rich silt from the uplands and spread it over the fields. As in the Tigris-Euphrates valley, the flooding of the river came in the spring. The Indus, too, became so full of silt that the irrigation canals were finally choked with it. We do not know how much this may have had to do with the ending of the Indus civilization.

Why did the Indus River become so muddy? We can only guess, but here is a possible reason. The Indus people built with bricks. Wood must have been used as fuel in baking these bricks. For hundreds of years, the people cut down enormous numbers of trees on the surrounding hills and fed them to the kilns that baked the bricks. The hills were laid

bare. In the heavy rains, earth washed off the hills into the
many small rivers that flow into the Indus, and then into
the Indus itself.

A muddy river is only one of the things that can happen
when man changes the earth by stripping it of what he finds
growing on it, or by digging up the earth and planting his
seeds in it, carelessly.

Much too often, all through history, man has been careless
in his use of the land.

5: Man Changes the Land

When early man first hunted animals and gathered the seeds and berries that grew around him, he hardly changed the land at all. Of course, the soil itself was always changing in its own slow way. Plants, animals and insects died and became part of the earth, bacteria and fungi were always at work on the process of decay, earthworms loosened the soil as they burrowed through it. Thousands of small living things played their part in the making of fertile soil, just as they do now.

Man was simply a part of all this. Even when he learned to dig up the earth with his stick and with his stone hoe, he did not change it much. He cleared small patches of land and planted them, pulling up weeds and bushes that were in his way, or burning them off.

For a long time, people did not even try to stay in one place year after year. They grew their grain wherever they could for a few seasons and then moved on. The small patch of earth they had cleared would go back to grass or brush or forest. The natural changes of the soil would begin again. Very likely no one would grow anything on that patch of earth again for many years. No one needed it. There were so few people then, only a handful compared with the millions there are now. There was an abundance of fertile land for everyone.

When man settled in the valleys of the great rivers and cultivated the same land year after year, the soil began to change. Man has been changing the land he uses ever since.

He could not have done this without tools. The stone hoe was a tool, though not a very good one. Much more useful was the plow. This was invented so long ago that no one knows where it was first used, except that this must have happened in the moist earth of the river valleys. The early plow was not strong enough to dig into hard earth.

The Egyptians lengthened their hoe and used two oxen to pull it. This became their plow. Miles of land could be turned over with the plow drawn by oxen, much more than one man pushing the same plow could do.

There is no more important invention than the plow in the history of man.

How, then, did the land change? When men learned to plow their fields and keep them plowed, nature no longer controlled the changes in the soil. Men were learning how to use their land. They were also learning how to misuse it.

Misuse of the land was really no one's fault at first. People had no idea that there was a right and a wrong way to use the earth. Long fertile miles of it stretched before them, ready to grow the good grain men needed, if only they did their work well and found the right magic to please the gods who made things grow.

People knew very little about the way nature took care of the earth. For thousands of years they did not know that the soil needs the dead things of earth returned to it, for the slow making of more living things. They did not know that animal refuse and manure should be given back to the earth. All these things happen in nature, but men had not seen this. Or perhaps they simply did not understand.

When men plowed straight up and down a hill, it did not occur to them that the next rain might wash half the earth off it, right down the furrows, and that after several rains the hill would be a bare and useless place where nothing could grow. If they had known this, they would probably have plowed straight up the hill anyway. They were proud of their straight furrows. There were plenty of other hills to plow, and people were not used to looking ahead to other summers, to other people who might use the same hill.

There were plenty of valleys, too. In the valleys where the early civilizations grew up, the land needed very little care. Year after year the grain grew tall there. The land was never worn out. Every year the rivers renewed it with layers of rich silt.

The people of the valleys did not know where this rich silt came from. The Egyptians gave thanks to the god of the Nile, Hâpi. At the height of the Nile flood they celebrated with a festival in honor of Hâpi. They chanted:

"Hail to thee, O Hâpi! Thou givest life to all Egypt, because of the silt and the rich smooth soil which thy river brings to us out of the southern regions! Lord of the valley of the Nile art thou, O Hâpi, lord . . . of the grain that grows after the waters have retreated and seed has been planted. Thou, Hâpi, art lord . . . of unnumbered products of the soil; lord, too, of fruit-giving trees, of cattle and sheep and goats and all living animals that succor man. Hail to thee, O Hâpi, hail!"

The Babylonians and the people of the Indus valley, too, sang the praises of the gods who had given them such fertile earth. There was no need to know where it came from. The faraway beginnings of the river itself were a mystery which was surely known only to the gods.

But silt in a river always comes from somewhere. Any river carries some. It is too much of it that causes trouble.

As we have seen, the silt in the Tigris and Euphrates rivers came from the bare hills to the north, where sheep and goats cropped the slopes too close, and too many trees were cut down.

In the Indus valley, the silt may have come from the uplands that had been laid bare by the cutting down of huge forests.

This pattern was repeated in Egypt. The rich silt washed down in the Nile flood came from the mountains in the area now called Ethiopia, where torrents of rain poured down in the summer. Herdsmen and shepherds for hundreds of years burned off the scrub and forest from the land, so fresh grass could grow for their cattle to eat. They are still doing this today.

The tons of topsoil that washed off the mountains and down the river was a precious gift to the Egyptians. But it has been a great loss to the Ethiopians. Burning off scrub and forest is not even a good way to provide grass for cattle. The remaining soil becomes poorer and poorer.

This washing down of soil from the hills is one kind of erosion. Erosion in the mountains of Ethiopia helped make possible the great civilization of ancient Egypt.

It was erosion in the uplands that made the canals in the Tigris-Euphrates and Indus valleys fill up with silt, even though there was practically no erosion in the valleys.

The people in the valleys knew very little about the care of the land, beyond the plowing and planting and watering that gave them good harvests. They knew nothing about erosion at all. But if they had known about it, they still could not have stopped what happened. They did not control the land in the mountains beyond their valleys.

Many times the people who have damaged their own land or that of their neighbors did not know they were doing it. Other times, they have known just what they were doing to damage the land and they did it anyway. It might not make much difference in their lifetime. It has taken people a long time to learn to care what happens to other people in the future and the land on which they will live.

All through history, the way people have used the land has made a great difference in the lives of those who came after.

6: Erosion in Ancient Times

Most erosion is caused by wind and water over the land, wearing it away. Erosion goes on in nature, slowly, all the time. Without it there would be no world as we know it at all.

The formation of soil itself is partly a process of slow erosion. Rocks are broken down and sorted by wind and water. Old soil washes away or blows away. New soil is always forming by slow weathering of the rock beneath. It is as if the earth were always discarding its old worn-out skin and making a new one.

We cannot even imagine how slowly this happens. For thousands of years our earth has been making and remaking itself.

But man has speeded up this process of erosion. It is the plants that grow in the earth that hold the soil in place. Too often man has stripped the plants and trees off the earth and left it bare, at the mercy of wind and water. When this is done, soil that might, if left alone, be blown away in a century can disappear in a year or even in a day. There are places where this has happened.

Soil erosion was already a problem in ancient times. Nothing was done about it at first. People were careless with the land. Invaders swept through one country after another, destroying the planted fields and cutting trees off the hills.

There were many more people than there had been in early times, most of them living in the fertile places of the earth. It became less and less practical to use up one piece of land and move on to the next. Farmers had to learn how to take better care of the land. To them the soil was still a living thing, the source of their own life. They cared for it as best they could, using the little that they knew.

The Old Testament tells us of an ancient farming people having a hard time. When Moses led the Israelites out of Egypt, they wandered for forty years in the Arabian desert before reaching the "promised land." They were often discouraged, but they were sure that a good land waited for them. Moses told the people:

"For the Lord thy God bringeth thee into a good land, a land of brooks of water, of fountains and depths that spring out of valleys and hills; a land of wheat, and barley, and vines, and fig trees, and pomegranates; a land of oil olive, and honey; a land wherein thou shalt eat bread without scarceness, thou shalt not lack any thing in it . . ."

This was to be a very different land from the valley of the Nile:

"For the land . . . is not as the land of Egypt, from whence ye came out, where thou sowedst thy seed, and wateredst it with thy foot, as a garden of herbs:

"But the land, whither ye go to possess it, is a land of hills and valleys, and drinketh water of the rain of heaven."

Compared with the lush valley of the Nile, this was not a paradise, after all. But it was a long time since these people had seen the Nile. They had wandered too long in the desert, and this did seem "a land that floweth with milk and honey."

At first, most of the Israelites lived only in the hills of their promised land. Other people, the Canaanites, were already living in the small fertile valleys.

It was to these same hills, or those close by, that the patriarch Abraham had come hundreds of years before. On the grass in the clearings on the hills he had pastured his sheep and his cattle.

Abraham and the other earlier Israelites had lived a wandering life with their herds. But the Israelites who had followed Moses out of Egypt had had enough of wandering. They settled into the hills in the land of the Canaanites, cut down trees, built villages, and planted their gardens on the slopes.

But planting on slopes created problems. It was hard to prevent erosion. Many of the hills were covered with forests when these Israelites first came. Cutting down the forests was the first thing that caused erosion. Plowing made it worse. The Old Testament tells us that Job complained: "The waters wear the stones: thou [the Lord God] washest away the things which grow out of the dust of the earth; and thou destroyeth the hope of man . . ." Job was not the last person to blame God for what man himself had done.

The Israelite farmers learned to build flat terraces on the hillsides, to keep the rain from washing the soil away. These terraces were edged with heavy stone walls, and some of these walls are still in place.

Most stone walls, however, do not stay as they are forever unless they are taken care of. There were many wars over the land of the Israelites. Wandering shepherd people fought with the more settled farming people. Terraces were torn down. They had to be rebuilt so life could go on. But the time came when the terraces could no longer be rebuilt. The red earth washed off many of the slopes until only rock was left. Grain cannot grow where there is no soil. Villages were abandoned. This was no longer a place where people could live.

Sometimes there was drought; the "rain of heaven" did not fall. Jeremiah, in the Old Testament, mourned: ". . . the ground is chapt, for there was no rain in the earth, the plowmen were ashamed, they covered their heads. . . . And the wild asses did stand in the high places, they snuffed up the wind like dragons; their eyes did fail, because there was no grass."

Farther south is the Negev desert, which the Bible calls the South. Here various people settled at different times. Some of them learned to make the desert "blossom as the rose." At the bottom of the deep wells they dug, they found "springing water," that is, water to drink. They planted tamarisk and other trees which needed very little water. They planted olive trees and vines and surrounded each one with a little stone wall which collected enough dew from the air to keep the tree or vine alive. In a desert where the small amount of rain would come in sudden torrents, they would build walls and dams to hold the water back and store it when the rains did come, and they let the rains wash good soil from the hills onto their fields. This was using the erosion of the hills for their own advantage.

The little land of Palestine, home of the Israelites, was important in ancient times, a place crossed by the trade routes of Asia, Greece, and Africa. Along these routes traveled the spices and silks of China, the riches of frankincense and myrrh, pearls of the Persian Gulf, and the ivory and gold of Africa. The land was fought over and conquered by one set of invaders after another. Through hundreds of years and many battles the land was not cared for, until at last too much of the country and too many of the people were destroyed. Most of the Israelites, who by that time were called the Jews, fled and were scattered through other countries. Palestine became a wasteland.

The modern state of Israel is changing this. The people there are reclaiming the land, building their farms in the little valleys and on some of the slopes. They are making gardens in the desert. You will read more about this in another chapter.

In ancient Greece, erosion had an even greater effect on the lives of the people than it did in Palestine. Greece was divided into city-states, each with its own independent government. The greatest of these was Athens, in the part of Greece called Attica.

The hills of Attica had been stripped of trees and used for planting long before Greece developed the great civilization which gave so much to the world. Waves of people had invaded Attica from the east and the north, too many for such a small area.

Good soil was washed off the hillsides by the rains. The soil that was left was used to grow too much. Its minerals were being used up. Before long, the land was so poor that Attica was not worth conquering. Other Greek cities went to war with their neighbors because they wanted more space for their people. But for a long time no one bothered Athens. No one wanted that worn-out land.

Plato, the great philosopher, wrote about his country: "What are now her [bare] mountains were lofty, soil-clad hills; her so-called shingle plains of the present day were full of rich soil; and her mountains were heavily afforested— a fact of which there are still visible traces. There are mountains in Attica which can now keep nothing but bees, but which were clothed, not so very long ago, with fine trees producing timber suitable for roofing the largest buildings . . ."

In the long run, the condition of the soil of Attica proved disastrous. But for a time there were advantages for Athens in being left alone. There was time for the people to live in peace and think about the world around them, time for the rulers to plan good government.

Outside of the city, most of the farmers owned their own land. Like the Israelites, they learned to build terraces on the hillsides. They used a digging tool called a mattock, and plows made from forked branches of trees, drawn by oxen.

These were fairly good farmers. There was enough rain most years and they did not need to irrigate the land. Half the fields were cultivated each year and the other half left alone, so nature itself could replenish them by growing wild grasses and weeds and letting them die and decay in the living earth.

Whatever these farmers could do for the land was not enough. The soil had been ruined before they ever sowed their grain in it. There were more people in Attica than the grain grown on this poor soil could feed.

Olive trees, fig trees, and grape vines will grow in poor soil. These were planted on the hillsides. But trees grow more slowly than grain. Many farmers lost their farms because they could not afford to wait for the trees and the vines to bear fruit.

In earlier times, it would have been impossible for people to survive on such poor soil at all. No early civilization could have developed in Egypt or Mesopotamia if the people had had to depend on the thin soil of washed-down hills for their grain. But times had changed. The Athenians continued to eat bread as well as meat. If they could not grow enough grain to feed themselves, they would get it elsewhere. They traded their olives and the wine made from their grapes with other cities and countries in exchange for grain.

The Athenians prospered. People today still study the science and philosophy of the ancient Greeks. We read their poetry and their plays. Their mythology and the epic poems, the *Iliad* and the *Odyssey*, have become a part of our own culture.

This prosperity and this culture depended on keeping grain flowing into Attica. A huge navy was built to bring in the grain and carry the products of Attica to other lands. As time went on, there were wars for grain and wars for more space where the increasing numbers of people could live.

Athens had grown great in spite of the poor soil on the hills of Attica. But her greatness did not last. Athens was no longer a city no one wanted to conquer. And the conqueror had a drastic weapon to use: cutting off the supply of grain.

Athens was conquered by the nearby city of Sparta, whose main activity was making war. More than two hundred years later, all of Greece, including Sparta and Athens, was conquered by the armies of Rome and became part of the Roman Empire.

7: Land Use: the Roman Empire

The ancient Romans did many things well. They built magnificent roads and aqueducts for carrying water. In their cities they put up beautiful buildings of marble and adorned them with sculpture. They were so good at making war that they conquered most of the known world of that time. They brought their own kind of progress to most of the lands they conquered, but they were stern masters over the people.

The Romans were good farmers, too. They knew a good deal about the care of the soil. They learned to use animal manure to fertilize it. They practiced crop rotation, as the Greeks did; that is, they left some of the fields unplanted for a season and then used them the next. They had still not learned the value of plowing green plants into the soil to enrich it.

Much of the land the Romans farmed did not have enough rain. They worked out efficient ways of watering the dry places.

And yet, the Romans did not know quite enough. The land they depended on the most, in their own home territory, Italy, did wear out. So did some of their conquered land. This wearing out of the land may even have been one reason for the fall of the Roman Empire, when the Vandals swept down from the north and sacked the city of Rome in the fifth century A.D.

What happened to the Roman land? It was fertile land, though it did not go deep. But it did not stay fertile. Erosion helped wear out the land. Too many trees were cut off the hills. Soil washed down into the rivers. But mainly what happened to the Roman soil was that it was used too long without being restored.

The early settlers had cleared the land by burning off the forest and the scrub. This is a convenient way of clearing and has been used by many people all over the world. We have seen that the Ethiopians cleared land for pasture in this way. If it is done often, it is not good for the land. The top layer of soil, which is always in the process of making itself, is destroyed. Dead plants in the soil are burned, along with the living plants. Many of the living organisms in the soil are killed.

Even so, the Roman land was used for growing food for a long time. It was the fertility of the soil that had made Rome powerful in the first place. It might have been kept fertile if other things had not happened to it.

The Roman state gave land for farming to soldiers returning from the wars. This was generous, but the farms the state gave were too small. Both the farmer and his land were overworked as he tried to get a living from it. Later there were larger farms owned by nobles and worked by many slaves. These, too, became overworked.

The Romans saw what was happening. They tried to stop erosion by putting in elaborate drains to carry water off the hillsides. They tried to take good care of every inch of fertile soil they had. Soil to the Romans was sacred, as it was to all ancient people.

Still, crop after crop was wrung from the land, without renewing it enough. Grain must be grown to feed the people. Many small farmers gave up. Their land became part of large farms managed mostly as a business. People who run large farms as a business often lose their feeling for the earth. The soil is considered a way of making money, not a source of life which must be well cared for so the people of the future can live on it, too. The small farmer who grew only enough food for himself and his family, with only a little to sell, lived much closer to the earth. He knew its value, not as money but as a living thing.

The soil the Romans used was wearing out. Erosion continued, too, as more of the hillsides were cleared for crops. The drainage works were clogged with silt. Water and debris poured down the unprotected hillsides. The Roman plain near the mouth of the Tiber River became the famous Pontine Marshes.

The Roman soil could no longer grow enough.

The rulers of Rome looked across the Mediterranean Sea to the city of Carthage, on the North coast of Africa. The Carthaginians were expert farmers. They grew miles of grain in their wide fields. They were even learning how to water the desert which surrounded them.

The Romans wanted that grain.

In a series of brutal wars they conquered Carthage. They burned the city and drove a plow through the ruins to symbolize their taking of the land.

The Romans took over the wide fields of North Africa. When they needed more land for growing food, they moved farther into the desert. The Romans devised wonderful ways of watering this desert. Long tunnels were dug to bring water from springs and streams in faraway hills. Huge stone cisterns stored water from the infrequent rains. Grain from

Tree roots exposed by soil erosion in a New York City park.

Soil profile. Dark rich topsoil above, less fertile subsoil
beneath, North Dakota.

Cattle grazing on good pasture, Tennessee.

Dust storm on an overgrazed cattle range, New Mexico.

Dust storm in southeastern Colorado, 1937.

A shelter belt planted on the Great Plains by the
Civilian Conservation Corps, North Dakota.

Sheet erosion on cornfield, showing the pattern of
planted rows, South Dakota.

Gulley erosion, Iowa.

the fields the Romans planted was sent in ships to Rome itself and to other parts of the empire.

Even this North African grain was not enough. The whole
Roman Empire was growing weak, for many reasons. It cost
too much to keep it all together. In A.D. 455 the Vandals
from the north sacked and burned Rome itself, and in 467
a barbarian chieftain became King of Rome.

The Vandals moved in, in great numbers, bringing their
families. They might have taken over the Roman water supply system and engineering works and their ways of cultivating the fields. They might even have tried to restore the
worn-out earth. But they did none of these things. They did
not care for the Roman government or art or engineering.
They used the land, but they did not care whether they used
it well.

At least, they did not care at first. But if they were to continue living on this land, they, too, must learn how to use it.
All over Europe, the Roman way of using the land was never
quite forgotten.

8: Land Use in the Middle Ages

Ancient Rome was the greatest power on earth for just a few centuries. After the Roman Empire came the period of history in Europe called the Middle Ages, from the fall of Rome in the fifth century to the late fifteenth century—about a thousand years.

Life was not easy for most people in the Middle Ages. The splendor of Rome was gone. But the Church saved much of the learning of an earlier time. The monks in their monasteries copied the old books and wrote new ones. New ideas were growing in the Middle Ages, but they grew slowly, waiting for the next period of history in Europe, the Renaissance in the fifteenth century.

In all the thousand years of the Middle Ages, there was very little change in the way people used the land. Farmers turned over the soil with heavy plows pulled by a number of oxen. These cumbersome plows did not cut deep.

Farmers sowed their seed by hand. They harvested their grain with short straight scythes and small heavy sickles. The work was hard. For those who tilled the soil the work was never-ending in the planting and harvesting seasons, and scarcely any easier when the crops were growing.

Although there were few changes in the way the land was farmed in the Middle Ages, there were many in the way the land was divided up. In the days of the Roman Empire, all Europe, some of Asia Minor, and northern Africa were under one government. In the Middle Ages, all this was changed. The central government of Rome no longer existed. Europe was divided into many small countries. In each country, all the land was supposed to belong to the king. He divided the land among important people, the nobles who promised to serve him.

Of course, this did not happen in just the same way everywhere, and this pattern of land use did not begin at the same time in all countries. But there was a definite pattern.

The noble's land in the Middle Ages was called a manor. Each manor was like a small self-sufficient country. It had its own meadows, woods, fields, rivers, pastures, one or more villages, and a manor house or castle where the noble lived. The best farmland was reserved for the lord of the manor himself.

In the villages dwelt the peasants—the farmers and craftsmen, both free and nonfree. They lived in huts with walls made of woven wattles (long bendable poles), plastered over with mud. The floors of the huts were earth, the roofs were thatch. The hard-working peasants cultivated their lord's farms in return for strips of land on which they could grow their own grain and vegetables.

Some of the peasants who were not freemen could not leave the manor without the lord's consent. On the other hand, the law held that the land the peasants worked could not be taken away from them. If they worked hard, there was just a chance that they might become rich enough from the produce of their fields to buy their freedom. This was a small chance. Many peasants were not interested in finding better ways to work. It was so unlikely that they could do anything to improve the way they lived.

Some of the open land on the manor was kept in grass for pasture where all the cattle of the manor grazed. The farm land was divided into three parts. One part would be sowed with wheat or barley, another with beans or oats, and the third would be allowed to lie unplanted, or fallow. The following year, each third would be given a different use, perhaps the wheat fields planted with beans, the fallow land planted with wheat, and the beans and oats fields of the year before left fallow. Animal manures were dug into the soil.

This kind of rotation kept the soil from wearing out, except very slowly. The land was not overworked. Men and soil were kept in balance, at least in western Europe, through most of the Middle Ages.

The climate helped the peasant. It was a good climate for growing crops, in most of Europe. Almost always there was enough rain, gentle rain, and summer was long enough.

On the manor, strips of land which the peasant could use were scattered over the three different sections of land. Often the peasants worked together on all the land, instead of walking from strip to strip. But the lord's land must be cared for first.

Farming was done this way for years and years. To most nobles and peasants it seemed the only way. At any rate, it was easiest to keep on farming the way it had always been done.

During most of the Middle Ages, the planted fields were left open, marked off only by lines of plowing, with borders of sod between the strips. There was nothing to keep cattle or sheep from running over the fields, helping themselves to the grain. Hunters, too, would trample the new grain.

Later, part of the land was divided up into permanent

farms and fenced in. It was easier to try new ways of farming on fenced-in land.

When he was not too tired to think, the peasant knew the worth of the land. Deep in his bones was a feeling of worship for the earth that gave him life. As he plowed the warm soil in spring, he smelled the rich life in it. He watched the countless small creatures that lived in it. Sometimes he picked up a handful of soil and crumbled it in his fingers. In this earth he planted his seed and tended it, because he knew that without him it could not grow well, and without the good grain that grew from this earth he could not live. "God speed the plow and give us bread enow," said an old proverb.

But the peasant scarcely had the time or the energy to put his feelings into words. He could neither read nor write. He had few rights. The lords and the knights had all the power. They lived in fine houses and castles, sang songs to their ladies, and busied themselves with bloody wars. Most of them despised the poor peasants. They called them stupid and evil-smelling. Perhaps, after all, they felt a little guilty at living always by the labor of others.

It is no wonder that the unfree peasant, at the bottom of the social scale, did not always care how much food he grew. He had to spend most of his time working on someone else's land, and he was despised by the people for whom he worked.

The monks in their monasteries knew better than to despise the peasants. It was the monks who had kept alive some of the learning of ancient times and added their own wisdom to it. They knew that the Bible itself taught that work on the land is good. "The husbandman [farmer] that laboureth," says the Bible, "must be first partaker of the fruits."

There were many terrible famines. Storms of hail washed away the grain, or too much was spoiled by the trampling and nibbling of animals. Sometimes the cattle died of a plague. Soldiers in the many wars trampled the fields and ruined the growing grain. People had to depend on what was grown on the land of their own manor. If there was too little, it was the peasants who went hungry.

But the land in Europe remained. During the thousand years of the Middle Ages the land was used for growing food the same way, over and over again. This was not the best way to use the land, but it was certainly not the worst. For one thing, there were never more people than the land could feed without being overworked. Many people were killed in wars, many died of terrible plagues and famines.

The land was not often used to grow crops to sell. It was used to grow food for those who lived on it, each manor separately. There was no need to force more growth from the soil than it could give and still remain fertile.

Toward the end of the Middle Ages there were a few changes. There were those who suggested planting clover and other special plants on the land that had been left fallow, and plowing them into the soil. They would then decay and help make new rich soil. This way of enriching the soil is called green manuring.

The most important improvements in farming were developed first in Holland and nearby countries, the Low Countries. This was the area where the medieval system of land ownership first started to change. Many farmers there owned their own farms or rented them on a permanent basis from townspeople who owned them. It pays to take good care of the soil on your own farm. The farmers of the Low Countries were neither the first nor the last to learn this.

Gradually the changes in land ownership and in farming

methods spread to other countries. Land is no longer owned or farmed in Europe just as it was in the Middle Ages. But here and there in the world of today the pattern of land ownership is still much like that of the Middle Ages. We call this pattern feudalism, a term we like to think belongs to the long ago.

The way people use their land has a great deal to do with the way they live. This has often been a forgotten part of history. Somehow it has always seemed more important to keep records of kings and battles and heroes. The peasants had little to say, and the land does not speak at all.

9: Other Parts of the World

So far we have been talking about the land in only a few parts of the world: Europe, North Africa, and the Middle East.

What about the rest of the world? Haven't people everywhere depended on the growing of grain and other plants in the earth they live on?

Not everywhere. There have been people who ate almost nothing but meat. The Eskimos of the Far North are the most obvious example. They may eat a few wild berries and roots in the summer months, but it is meat they depend on. Their cold country hardly allows for much contact with the land. They cannot become farmers.

In most parts of the world, however, the use of the land for growing food has had great importance in the lives of the people.

In China, civilization began somewhat later than it did in Egypt and Mesopotamia. The early Chinese civilization was built up on the kind of soil that is called loess. This is a fine earth deposited over wide areas by the wind, thousands of years ago. Our own Great Plains are covered with this kind of soil. It is a fertile soil.

The valleys of the great rivers, on the other hand, have a different kind of soil, alluvium. This is soil brought down and deposited by rivers. As we have seen, this is the most fertile soil of all.

The Chinese loess is a yellow earth covering miles and miles of plains and slopes. For thousands of years the early Chinese people lived on this earth and cultivated it. They dug up the grass that grew there. They attacked the soil with digging sticks, stone hoes, and plows. They did not want the grass that had always grown on this soil. Grass is good only for the grazing of animals such as cattle, and these people kept no cattle. Milk, cheese, and beef had no part in their diet. So the miles of good earth were given over to the growing of millet in early times, later to wheat, rice, and barley.

The increase in the number of people living on this earth was tremendous. More and more grassy land was plowed. Trees were cut off the wooded slopes so hills, too, could be plowed. And erosion began. Little ditches formed across the fields in the rain. Ditches became gullies. Some gullies became canyons. The yellow earth was washing away.

These Chinese were good farmers, in spite of what happened to the land. They tried to stop the ruin of their soil. They built irrigation systems in dry places, but in time the canals filled up with silt. They made careful terraces—steps of earth—on the slopes, to keep the earth from washing away.

They had to use the land to feed the people. They could not have fed such tremendous numbers of people on this land at all if they had not been expert farmers. But after all, they could not do enough for the land. Millions of acres of land in northern China have become worn out and worthless through the years. Thousands of people have died in terrible famines.

There were too many people on the land. The balance of nature could not be maintained.

The Yellow River (Hwang Ho) has carried the burden of tons of silt from this land for centuries. It fills up its own bed with silt and overflows in devastating floods. Millions of Chinese farmers for thousands of years have built dikes beside the river, piling up the earth with their bare hands and in baskets, to keep the river where it belongs. The level of the river has risen until it is higher than most of the land around it.

Now there are still more millions living on this land, and they must struggle somehow with the earth they have inherited from their ancestors of ancient times. It would not be fair to these ancestors to say they did not care. They loved the land. They tried to use it well. They could not possibly have foreseen what devastation would be caused by their simple hoes and plows as they cut into the earth.

In an entirely different part of the world, in the section of South America which is now Peru, lived the Indians we call Incas. We think of the Inca civilization as an early one, because of the way the people lived. Actually, this civilization existed much later than that of ancient Greece and Rome, toward the end of the medieval period in Europe. In ancient times, there was no contact at all between people in far-apart areas of the world. The people who lived in South America at the time Greece and Rome flourished could not possibly have known anything about these civilizations. The Incas could not possibly have heard of medieval Europe.

The story of the Incas in Peru lasted only about three hundred years, until the Spanish explorers conquered them in the sixteenth century A.D. The Indian cultures of Peru, before the Incas came, in about A.D. 1200, lasted more than fifteen hundred years.

The Incas developed a complicated civilization, a smoothly working government, and interesting art. But what we are concerned with here is their use of the soil.

The story of the Incas and their land is entirely different from the story of land in ancient Greece and Rome. It is not much like the story of the use of the land in early Egypt and Mesopotamia. It is a story of man making a fertile soil for his own use and keeping it so.

In the Inca civilization, individual people did not own any land at all. Land was divided into three groups: First, land belonging to the Sun, which meant the state religion. This land was used for temples and festivals and by the priests as their own source of grain and vegetables. The largest amount of land belonged to the second group, the people themselves, all of them together. The third group of owners was the state itself, that is, the rulers, who were the only people then called the Incas, and their families.

The people worked together on all the land, first on the state land, then on the lands of the Sun, and finally on their own. But though no individual owned land, each head of a family was given the harvest from a particular piece of land for the use of himself and his wife. Besides this, he was given the harvest of an additional piece of land for each of his children. He was sure of having enough for his family to eat, though he must work on all the land with all the people of his village.

These people had no plow, and no animals that might have pulled one. They worked together across the fields in two long rows, one of men and one of women, chanting while they loosened the earth with digging sticks.

This system may not have encouraged individual initiative, but the Incas must have felt that it worked very well. For the first time in history, everyone had enough to eat all the time.

On their land the Incas grew a great number of foods, all of them different from those growing in Europe and the Middle East (Egypt and Mesopotamia) and the Far East (China) in ancient times. What they grew most was maize, the good Indian corn which was known also to the North American Indians. They grew potatoes, too, and sweet potatoes, yams, squash, and other vegetables. Europeans had never eaten any of these vegetables before the explorers brought them back from North and South America.

Long before the time of the Incas, Indians had planted their seeds in the rich soil of the little valleys of Peru, beside the streams that ran into the Pacific Ocean. Here there was not much rain, but the small streams overflowed their banks and irrigation canals were dug into the little valleys. The streams brought down fertile soil from the mountains, as the Nile did in Egypt, but much less of it. These were small streams, and there was not much erosion in the mountains the streams came from.

Before long, there were too many people trying to live on the fertile soil of these little valleys. So the whole barren strip of desert along the coast was irrigated. Water of mountain streams was stored in vast stone reservoirs in the hills and led down to the coast in aqueducts. There it ran into the long canals that brought water to the growing fields.

Then the soil was fertilized with manure of animals and the guano of seabirds. All the parts of crops that were not eaten were dug back into the earth. Maize was planted by making a hole and dropping in a fish head for fertilizer, and two or three seeds. This was a rich earth and the Incas kept it so.

Still more land was needed. The Incas moved up into the Andes Mountains. Earlier people had already built terraces around these mountains, following the contours of the land much as contour plowing does today. The Incas built still more and better terraces, moving higher and higher up the mountainsides as they needed food for more people.

This is how the terraces were made: Long parallel walls of stone were built around the mountains, curving with the shape of the slopes. The space behind the walls was filled in with earth which was carried there, often from long distances, and pressed tight against the walls. These terraces transformed the mountainsides into thousands of little fields for planting.

There was almost no erosion on these mountainsides. The soil on the mountains and in the valleys was never worn out.

There was time for these people, too, to think of more than just the business of keeping alive. Beautiful wooden and clay jars were made. Both the men and women were expert weavers of colorful textiles made of cotton and wool.

The religion of these people was an agricultural one. Here, too, the soil itself was considered sacred. The Earth was the mother-goddess of all things. The people prayed thus:

> "Mother of all things,
> Let me, too, be thy child."

When the Spanish conquerors came looking for gold in the sixteenth century, they destroyed the whole way of living of these people. It was no longer possible to care for the earth, to keep the dry valleys watered and the terraces planted. The wonderful civilization of the Incas was gone forever. It has been a long and complicated job for archaeologists to find out about this civilization, because the Incas never developed a system of writing. Some of the Spaniards who were not so interested in gold did write down what they found of interest in the lives of these people. Some of them, too, understood and appreciated the way in which the Incas had cared for the land. Without the records of these Spaniards we would know very little about the Incas today.

The Inca success with their land was not repeated in the history of any early civilization in the Americas.

Let's see what happened to the land of the Mayas in Central America. These people developed a civilization in which the nobility and priests lived well, farmers had slaves, and most of the people worked hard for the benefit of the few who did not work. The achievements of these few, with the help of their slaves, were considerable. Mayan art is one of the wonders of archaeology.

But this civilization had developed only in spite of the most primitive use of the land, and it was already collapsing when the Spanish conquerors came.

Here, too, the plow was never invented. To clear the land, jungle trees and brush were cut down and burned. (This is called slash and burn.) Much of the unprotected soil washed away in the heavy rains. Maize and other plants were planted in this earth. Some natural manures were used as fertilizer, but the land was soon worn out and had to be left alone a long time before it could be used again. In this hot tropical climate, it would go back to jungle. Meanwhile the farmer would have to move on and make another clearing.

The time came when all the land around the cities was used up. Farmers had to go farther and farther into the jungle to find woodland that could be cleared. When their cities were completely surrounded by miles of burned and worn-out land, the Mayas abandoned them and built new cities in an entirely different place.

Jungles grew over the old cities and hid them from human eyes. It is only in recent years that archaeologists have uncovered them and found the great stone sculpture and massive architecture of these people.

We do not know for certain that it was the worn-out land that made the Mayas abandon their great cities and build new ones elsewhere. Although the Mayas did have a written language, they left no explanation of the uprooting of their cities. But archaeologists think that this must have been the reason they moved. In the same way, the first farmers, anywhere in the world, moved on from a piece of worn-out land to a fresh one.

As we move farther north, to our own part of the continent of North America, we will find still another story of the use of the land, one which must be of great concern to us today, because this is where we live.

10: The Land: Early U.S.A.

It was a bright morning in the month of May, in the year 1607. Three small sailing vessels moved slowly up a broad tidal river in what is now the state of Virginia. For six months the men on these ships had battled winter cold and wild storms on the Atlantic Ocean. Now they looked out at the deep forests and lush meadows along the banks of the river. They looked, and rejoiced, and gave thanks. This was indeed a good piece of earth. In England, an earlier explorer had written of this land: "The soil is the most plentifull, sweete, fruitfull and wholesome of all the worlde."

As soon as the men had found a place they thought would be good for a settlement, they tied up their ships and went ashore. A fort was built first, for defense against the unknown. Then there was a church, a storehouse, and log huts to live in. This was Jamestown.

After a few buildings had been finished, the settlers should have plowed the land and planted seeds, so there might be a good harvest and enough to eat for the next year. The food they had brought with them was nearly used up. But these men were not farmers. They had come to the New World to get rich. Instead of plowing, they hunted for gold.

They searched for a passage to China. They quarrelled among themselves and with the Indians. It was only after a disastrous year of disease and starvation that the settlers of Jamestown realized they would have to get to work and raise crops. Only the land could keep them alive. Most of the settlers would just have given up if it had not been for the strong leadership of John Smith.

Many things went wrong. The settlers found they had not chosen a good piece of land after all. They had tried to build their town on a swampy peninsula where there was not even good water to drink.

There was better land near by. Though these settlers did not appreciate it, they had for their use an unusually good piece of the rich earth of the New World, until now almost untouched by human hands. Here they learned to plow, plant their seeds, and reap good harvests.

A few years later, in December of 1620, another small wooden ship, battered by howling storms in the North Atlantic, dropped anchor off what was to become the little town of Plymouth, Massachusetts. This ship was the *Mayflower*.

This time women came with the men, hoping for homes in a new land where all of them could practice their own religion. They looked out from their ship to see what kind of place they had come to. It was winter, and the wind was cold. Here were no lush meadows, and though there were evergreens in the forests, most of the trees were bare.

These patient people had hoped for something quite different from this. They had heard of the rich land in Virginia and they themselves had intended to land on the shores of Delaware Bay. Columbus had written about the land of North America: "Always the land was of the same beauty, and the fields very green and full of an infinity of fruits as red as scarlet, and everywhere there was the perfume of flowers and the singing of birds, very sweet."

Columbus had never seen the cold and cheerless winter shore where the *Mayflower* landed. It seemed impossible to live on this land. But the long voyage was over, and the people gave thanks for that.

There were trees for the building of houses. And after the long winter spring came. This spring was a miracle of greenness, suddenly covering the earth that had seemed so cold and dead under the winter snow. There were green fields, bright flowers, and the singing of birds that came from the south.

The Pilgrims of Plymouth plowed the brown earth and planted corn and other crops. Friendly Indians helped.

These pioneers had sailed across three thousand miles of wild ocean to find peace and freedom. In the New World there was at first only one way in which they could prosper, and that was by use of the land. There were endless miles of land, it seemed. Surely this would sustain them. It did, but there were hard years at first. Some of the Indians were enemies. There was disease and death from bad water, bad food, and the cold. And sometimes the crops the people planted did not bring a good harvest.

All these land-hungry colonists came from the over-crowded cities of Europe. America was their promised land. In fact, these people had more in common with the Israelite farmers who had settled in the hills of the promised land of Judea, more than two thousand years before, than they had with the Indians they found living in North America in 1620.

The colonists used wooden plows to turn over the earth. They planted European wheat and harvested it with sickles, as farmers had done in Europe for hundreds of years, and as the Israelites had done even longer ago.

The American Indians, on the other hand, lived very much as the stone-age people had lived in Europe, many thousands of years before. Their tools were stone axes, fire-hardened sticks, and clamshells. They were part-time gardeners who lived also by hunting and fishing.

So we see that it was not only the land that was strange and new to the colonists. Even stranger were the people who lived on this land and used it in ways the colonists could not understand. From these people the colonists learned to grow the maize which kept them from starvation.

The Indians had a primitive way of living, but they were not less intelligent than the Europeans. It simply had not occurred to them, as yet, to change their surroundings very much. They liked things the way they were. The rich earth and the forests that provided game gave them good health and peace of mind. Deer were their cattle. They gathered wild nuts and berries in the woods. They grew a little maize.

There were many tribes of Indians in North America. Of course, they did not all have the same customs or even exactly the same ways of using the land. Some were more civilized than others. But none of them did any permanent damage to the land.

The Indians cleared small areas of land for their maize, and then moved on to other fields. They never left miles of cleared land lying uncovered or cut all the trees off a hillside, so the rain could wash the good topsoil off it. They did sometimes light fires at the edge of the prairie, burning off the forest that might gradually have grown over it. Preserving the prairie in this way was good not only for the Indians but for the white people who later planted it with miles of corn and wheat.

When the white men came, this North American earth had known no erosion but the natural slow erosion of nature.

It is only recently that we have begun to appreciate the way in which the Indians preserved the land. There were very few of them, compared to the numbers of people living on this continent today, just one Indian, on an average, for hundreds of acres of land. There was no need for them to try to force more food from the earth than nature could easily grow. The gardens of maize made very little difference.

As with other primitive people, the Indian women did the farming. The Indians knew that the soil itself gave them life. To them, as to many early people, the earth was their Great Mother. The Indians were not impressed by the plow brought by the European colonists. They refused to use it. Running a plow through the earth seemed to them like wounding their Earth Mother with a knife.

The Indians had no understanding of individual land ownership at all. Land was given by the Great Spirit to everyone, like the air and the water. People should live with the land as its children, take care of it, and defend it. They could never sell it, the Indians believed, because it was not really theirs.

When Indians took payment from white people for land, they meant only to offer its use for the growing of food. They knew that white people must use the land in order to survive, just as they did. The Indians would never have "sold" land to the white people if they had understood what ownership meant to them, or if they had had any idea how destructive the white man could be in his use of the earth.

In the Europe which most of the colonists came from, there were many more people living on the land than in North America. Land for farming was scarce. It had been divided up, used and changed, over and over again. Most of the land was owned by the fortunate few. The many who were less fortunate worked on land that would never be their own. Many, too, had lost their rights to use the land at all.

With this background, it was impossible for the colonists to understand the Indians' way of thinking about the land. They knew only that here were miles and miles of untouched fields and forests, land they could own and farm as they wished. There was plenty for everyone. It looked as if there would always be plenty.

They were wrong. On the whole earth there is not enough land unless we use it well.

11: The Land Is Worn Out:
Eastern U.S.A.

In all the history of man, there has never been anything like the destruction of the earth that has taken place on the North American continent. In just three hundred years, in many parts of this country, soil that nature built up over a period of thousands of years has been ruined, sometimes in less than a year.

The early colonists did not know what they started. They were concerned with their own survival. Some of the colonists had been farmers in Europe; others had not. The kind of farming they had known in Europe involved careful use of limited amounts of farmland. The soil there was heavy and the climate favorable, with gentle rains. Crops were rotated much as they had been in the Middle Ages, and in many places the soil was enriched with animal manures and green manure. The land was still cared for best in the lowlands and other countries on the mainland of Europe. The English farmers were a little behind. This was to make a difference in their care of the soil in the New World.

European farming was good farming. What happened when these people settled in America? For one thing, the soil in America was not the same as in Europe. It was lighter and washed away more easily in the heavy rains. This problem, however, could have been overcome. The colonists were careless with the land mostly because there was so much of it. There just seemed to be no end to the rich earth and the vast forests. The easiest way to farm was to use up one patch of land and move on to the next.

This was the way early man had farmed. It didn't matter then. There were so few people in early times that their simple method of farming could not possibly do any real harm to the earth. Neither could the gardens planted by the American Indians.

The Europeans brought the plow and the sickle and they farmed with a vengeance. News of the fertile earth of the New World was carried home to Europe, and more and more people came.

Rotation of crops was forgotten. There didn't seem to be any need for it. Any piece of land was all right to use. Trees were cut down wherever they were needed for building, or wherever they just happened to be in the way. Sometimes whole forests were burned.

It was all too easy. The earth, it seemed, was made for the use of man. It didn't matter how he used it. Most people had forgotten the old rituals, the old feeling that the earth was sacred because it was the source of life itself. Most of the newcomers did not share the Indians' reverence for the Great Mother.

In all fairness, it must be said that the colonists did not intend to destroy the land. There was nothing in their previous experience to tell them what might happen when the rains poured down on miles of plowed sloping earth. They could not have known, either, that thousands of people would keep coming to this continent, until there was no longer enough good new land for everyone.

People used the earth because they needed it, for growing food, for building houses, for earning a living. It was cheaper to use it up and move on than to take good care of the land. Everyone was doing it. At least, nearly everyone.

People in the early Dutch and English colonies in America had their passage paid for by trading companies. They were supposed to repay the companies by producing a profit for them. In the New England colonies, fishing and lumbering made enough profit in the early years. In New Amsterdam there were furs from up the Hudson River. Land was used only to feed the people who lived there, and the soil was somewhat better cared for than in many other areas. Much of it was farmed the wrong way, just the same. In any case, this had never been the richest soil on the continent.

The story was different in Virginia and in other southern colonies. There, the earth itself was used for profit. Europeans wanted tobacco. It grew well in the rich soil of the South. Year after year, crop after crop, tobacco was grown on the land and sent to England.

Year after year, trees were cut down for lumber and the making of turpentine. There were more and more herds of cattle, hogs, and horses. They ate off acres of grass.

Before the seventeenth century was over, a few people could see what was happening. Anyone could see that there were more and more floods. There weren't enough trees on some of the slopes to hold back the water in a heavy rain.

Tobacco drained the riches from the land and left it exhausted. Too much of the organic matter in the soil was gone. Soil that had been rich and dark was light-colored now, no longer fertile. Rivers ran red with the red-brown soil of the South. It didn't pay to plant the same land with tobacco for more than three or four years.

Land was cleared, used a few years, and abandoned.

Thomas Jefferson was concerned about this. He wrote, "We can buy an acre of new land cheaper than we can manure an old one." Jefferson himself used what he called "horizontal plowing" on his slopes, to prevent erosion. This is plowing across, to fit the curve of the land, the "contour plowing" of today. Jefferson urged other farmers to plow this way, too. "We now plow horizontally," he wrote, "following the curvature of the hills and hollows on dead level, however crooked the lines may be. Every furrow then acts as a reservoir to receive and retain the waters; scarcely an ounce of soil is now carried away . . . In point of beauty nothing can exceed that of our waving lines and rows winding along the face of our hills and valleys."

Most farmers did not agree with this. They liked the looks of their straight furrows, even if they went downhill and turned into water channels. For years, plowing in a straight line had meant good farming.

In 1798, to save his land, George Washington gave up cultivating corn and, instead, bought it elsewhere. Patrick Henry said, soon after the Revolution, "He is the greatest patriot, who stops up the most gullies."

There were others who talked of better farming methods, crop rotation, ways of preventing erosion, even terracing of land on steep slopes. Some farmers listened, but they were few. What was the use of taking care of this land? It didn't pay. People had heard about all the land there was to the West. Explorers had been there, Daniel Boone and others. They talked about forested hills and green valleys. A few families had moved West already. Others dreamed about a new life on that limitless rich land.

Some towns just disappeared as the land wore out. Dumfries, Virginia, was one of these. The town had been settled in 1690, on Quantico Creek, which flows into the Potomac

River. Before long it became the largest tobacco trading center in northern Virginia. People there were prosperous. Life was full of many pleasures. Splendid colonial mansions were built. George Washington often visited friends there. But the land around Dumfries, where so much tobacco had been grown, was washing away. Quantico Creek was filling up with it. Finally, at the time of the Revolution, the creek was so full of silt that it seemed more mud than water. Tobacco could no longer be grown on the fields. Now Dumfries is a little village of five hundred people.

Where did the people of Dumfries go? Most of them went West, probably. West was where there was plenty of good new land.

In the East, rain washed the furrows into gullies on deserted fields.

12: Going West

In the early days of this country, the real pioneer was the farmer. It was the farmer who settled in the wilderness we now call the Middle West. Usually he took his wife with him and children were born as they worked together on the new land.

Clearing land was hard work. In wooded regions, trees had to be cut down and stumps dug out of the earth. Logs made from these trees were used to build cabins to live in. When that was done, clearing trees off the land could be done an easier way. Bark could be cut off trees in a circle, all around the trunk. This girdling killed the trees. Dead trees burned easily. The waste was terrific. Great logs of oak, hickory, birch, walnut, and wild cherry that had been growing for years simply went up in smoke. The timber that was wasted would have been worth millions of dollars today. It seemed worthless then, just something to be gotten out of the way.

Before the colonists arrived, a squirrel could travel through the treetops from the Atlantic coast to the Mississippi River without ever touching the ground. At least, so they say. No one knows whether a squirrel ever tried it. It is hard, now, to imagine our country so covered with forests.

Stephen Vincent Benét wrote of the pioneers in his poem *Western Star:*

"And they looked to the West
and searched it with their eyes,
And there was the endless forest, and the sharp star."

The forest did not remain endless very long.

By the time the Revolutionary War was over, there were scattered settlements between the Appalachian Mountains and the Mississippi River. This was the West. The big river was its boundary.

Year after year, farmers grew the same crops on this fertile land, just as they had in the East. After several years of growing corn, a field might be worn out. Here, too, it didn't seem to matter. There was plenty of land. Clearing another field was hard work, but it was quicker and cheaper than trying to bring fertility back to the old field. Rain washed topsoil off the abandoned field before the weeds could grow on it. Rain washed topsoil off the new field, too, between the rows of corn planted straight up the slopes. Good soil washed into the creeks, down the creeks into the rivers, and finally out to sea. It would never return to the land. That didn't seem to matter, either, so long as there was somewhere to grow corn to eat and sell that year, and the next year. Very few people looked ahead to the years when other people would be making a living on this land.

The European tradition of taking care of your land so you could leave it in good condition for your children to use did not seem to apply here. Your children could have a new piece of land. It looked as if there would be enough farm land for people for at least another hundred years.

Through the pleasant fertile valleys roamed a small bearded man with a poke swung over his shoulder. He was called Johnny Appleseed. He was a sort of frontier saint even while he lived, and since he died his story has become an American legend. Johnny's poke was filled with seeds and plants. He was a friend of Indians and white people alike. Johnny would arrive in the evening at a farmhouse and have supper with the family. He sometimes preached a kind of sermon on the love of nature and of all mankind.

Johnny's greatest interest in life was planting apple trees all along the frontier in Ohio and neighboring areas. He scattered seeds, gave them to settlers to plant, and started seedlings. In the fields and woods where he roamed you will still find wild spicy apples on trees descended from those planted by Johnny Appleseed. His apples will still be growing, on other trees, hundreds of years from now, and his legend will still be told.

Farther west was unknown territory. People had heard about the prairie and the Great Plains. The prairie was covered with tall lush grass, as high as a horse's stomach. Lewis and Clark, in 1806, brought back from their explorations of the Northwest a story of the short-grass plains farther west, where it seldom rained. Plains stretched from horizon to horizon. There were hot dry deserts that dried up everything but a few desert plants. Cold winter winds in the mountains would blow through you. Still farther, in the great Northwest, beyond the mountains, there was rich country for farming.

The Mississippi Valley began to seem crowded; there were villages less than ten miles apart. It was a little harder to make good now, with your neighbor maybe a better farmer than you.

People turned west again, first of all to the wide prairie. The central part of the Mississippi Valley, the land just west of it, south into Texas and north into Canada, is the prairie. This was a seemingly endless area, sometimes flat, sometimes rolling, green with long grasses. Trees and bushes grew only along the streams, where they found enough water. Wild flowers, gay with color, bloomed among the grasses of the prairie, windflowers in the spring, blue verbena, yellow sunflowers and goldenrod in the fall, and many others.

Carl Sandburg wrote, much later, speaking of the prairie, "I am the prairie, mother of men, waiting."

The prairie has meant many different things to different people. There were some who just hoped to get rich on their new farms on the prairie. It didn't often happen. There were others who thought that getting away to a new place and a new beginning would solve all their problems. Sometimes it did; more often not.

There were the Indians, who loved the prairie and knew its every mood, sunrise and sunset, winter and spring, this land of waving grass given by the Great Spirit to man, if he would use it well.

There is a Chippewa song that says:

> "As my eyes search the prairie
> I feel the summer in the spring."

Grass *was* the prairie. Willa Cather describes the prairie this way, in her novel, *My Antonia:*

"As I looked about me I felt that the grass was the country, as the water is the sea. . . . And there was so much motion in it; the whole country seemed, somehow, to be running."

Grass roots held tight the rich earth of the prairie. Carl Sandburg wrote of grass roots on the prairie:

"Grass clutches at the dark dirt with finger holds.
Let it be blue grass, barley, rye, or wheat,
Let it be Johnny-jump-ups springing clean blue streaks.
Grassroots down under put fingers into dark dirt."

It did not occur to the pioneers that it might not be a good thing to dig up the prairie grass. No one bothered to consider that without the grass roots the soil itself might not stay where it belonged. Everyone knew there was not as much rain on the prairie as there was in the forest lands of the East. That was why grass grew there instead of trees. But somehow no one was prepared for the years when there would not even be enough rain and the dry earth would start to blow.

There is a story from the prairie country of North Dakota about the turning over of the prairie sod. It is a true story, perhaps embroidered a little with time, about a new settler named John Christiansen.

One day John Christiansen was clearing sod on his land in North Dakota. He was working hard, turning the tough sod over with a plow. In the next field stood an old Sioux Indian, watching. Hours went by. The farmer felt a little uneasy, being watched. The Indian wasn't armed. But what did he want? Hours went by. The Indian stood there.

Finally Christiansen asked the Indian why he was watching. The Indian's reply was just three words. The farmer shrugged and went back to his work. What could that old Indian know about farming?

Years later, people were to remember those three words spoken by the Indian: "Wrong side up." They knew what he meant, every year when there was too little rain. Grass roots that were right side up would hold in the earth the rain that fell, however little it might be. But grass roots could not hold anything at all when they were wrong side up.

Wind blowing the topsoil off the dry prairie where the sod had been turned wrong side up was to become a disaster.

The Indians did not dig up the prairie grass. This was not where they planted their gardens. They hunted buffalo across the prairie and the flat plains, while there were buffalo to hunt.

But to the pioneers the rich earth of the prairie seemed a miracle sent from heaven. They need only get the tough prairie sod out of the way.

This was good farming land for those who used it well. It still is, today, some of the best farming land in the world. But it has deserved better treatment than it has often had.

It was so wonderful, in those pioneering days, to have land of your own. Some of these farmers did have a feeling of reverence for the earth. None of them meant to ruin the land they farmed. There was too much they did not understand and could not plan for.

Many, too, were not prepared for the hardships they would find. Winds howled around the houses all winter. There were blizzards some years. So much snow would blow out of the sky that houses disappeared under it entirely. People froze.

Some settlers gave up and went back East. Some died of disease and bad drinking water on the long journey West.

Others kept on. They dug their first shelters into the earth of the hillsides. Then they cut pieces of the sod out of the prairie, grass roots and earth baked hard in the sun. They stacked these pieces up to make their sod houses, warm in winter, cool in summer. After a summer rain or two the sod houses might blossom all over with bright wild flowers.

By this time, people were coming to America from many parts of Europe, not just England or Holland. In *Giants in the Earth*, O. E. Rölvaag wrote of some Norwegian families who settled on the prairie in South Dakota. Most of the men had been fishermen in Norway before they came to America. To the main character in the book, Per Hansa, farming the rich soil of the prairie seemed to be his destiny, the realization of the hopes of many years. He was in love with the earth. His wife, however, did not share this feeling. To her, this never seemed a fit place to live. There were others who felt as she did.

Per Hansa's first plowing on his own land was pure joy:

"Dragging the plow, he drove out for some distance toward the hillock, then stopped and looked around. This was as good a place as anywhere to start breaking . . . He straightened up the plow, planted the share firmly in the ground, and spoke to the oxen: 'Come now, move along, you lazy rascals!' He had meant to speak gruffly, but the thrill of joy that surged over him as he sank the plow in his own land for the first time, threw such an unexpected tone of gentleness into his voice that the oxen paid no attention to it; he found that he would have to resort to more powerful encouragement. . . . After a little, however, they began to stretch their muscles. Then they were off; the plow moved . . . sank deeper . . . the first furrow was breaking. . . .

". . . The sod, which had been slumbering there undisturbed for countless ages, was tough of fibre and would not give up its hold on the earth without a struggle. It almost had to be turned by main strength, piece by piece; it was a dark brownish colour on the under side—a rich black mould that gave promise of wonderful fertility; it actually gleamed and glistened under the rays

of the morning sun, where the plow had carved and polished its
upturned face. . . ."

The sod that had been "slumbering there undisturbed for
countless ages" was being broken up all over the prairie. No
one could foresee what would happen when this loose earth
began to blow in the wind.

While the prairie was being settled, things were happening farther west. In 1848 gold was discovered in California.
Thousands of people headed to the West. All sorts of people.
Farmers dropped their plows. Carpenters put down their
hammers. Storekeepers closed their shops. People who had
never succeeded anywhere were sure they'd succeed this
time.

Most went by land. Some went by sea. A few found gold.
Others died before they got there. Some settled down on
the rich land and became farmers.

The short-grass area of the Great Plains, west of the
prairie, still seemed too dry for farming. Maps made before
1860 called this region the Great American Desert.

It wasn't long before cattlemen discovered that the short
grass of the plains was fine feed for cattle. They moved in
by thousands. Cattle were herded on the grass of the plains
from the Missouri River to the Rocky Mountains, from the
Canadian border to Mexico. Life on the plains was rough
and hard, but it could be exciting, too. The dashing cowboy
on his horse is still a romantic figure in our movies and on
television.

After the cattlemen came the farmers and their families,
pushing them farther west. Much of the soil on the Great
Plains was rich and deep, good for growing wheat and other

crops. Some years there was enough rain, often enough so a man could hope for a good harvest.

In 1854 a half-million acres of the best prairie farmland in America, in the Minnesota Territory, had been sold to homesteaders by the government at $1.25 an acre. There were plenty of takers. Some of them were speculators who bought the land from the government and then resold it at a higher price.

This was only the beginning of homesteading in the West. In 1862 the United States Congress passed the Homestead Act. President Lincoln signed it. This Act gave to any citizen of the United States over twenty-one years of age a farm of 160 acres, free, if he would settle on the land and cultivate it for five years. The land for these farms was in the public domain, that is, it belonged to the Federal Government, which held it for the use of the people. Much of this land was on the Great Plains.

The government had chosen a good time to give land away. The Civil War had just ended. Many Southerners had lost everything they owned in their support of the war. Many people in the North were restless. To some of these people it looked as if going West would solve all their problems. They didn't think much about the new problems they would be running into.

There were Indians roaming the plains, as they had for hundreds of years. They had a better claim to the land than any white man. Much of the Indians' land had already been taken from them. Treaties had been signed guaranteeing them possession of what was left. But treaties with Indians were not considered binding by the white men. When they wanted more land, they took it. The Indians fought for the land with wild ferocity. The white men hunted them with equal ferocity and finally subdued them. Most of the Indians were driven into reservations they themselves would never have chosen. Many Indians on the Northern Plains were sent South. This was one of the less glorious aspects of our westward expansion. Another was the slaughter of all the buffalo on the plains. With the buffalo gone, the Plains Indians had lost their principal source of food and shelter.

More thousands of people went West. Before long it became clear that 160 acres was not enough land for a profitable farm on the vast plains. It wasn't enough for a cattle-raising ranch, either. Cattlemen staked out their 160 acres, then bought more land, if it was available. Or they used government land for grazing, without permission. This worked pretty well at first, before there were too many cattle.

Sheepherders took over some of the land. The sharp hoofs of sheep cut the earth. Sheep crop the grass too close. Grass was disappearing from miles and miles of the plains.

Homesteaders and cattlemen fought each other for the land. Cattlemen fought sheepherders. Homesteaders had no way of keeping the ranchers' cattle out of their fields of growing corn and wheat. Some of them gave up and went back East. Then barbed wire was invented. Fields could be fenced off to keep the cattle out.

There were droughts some years. There were plagues of grasshoppers. Many settlers left. But in good years, even more came to stake out their homesteads. Millions of acres were divided into farms.

Making a new start could be hard. It wasn't always possible to make a living at all. About this time, western farmers began to sing a song which has been sung by groups of farmers ever since:

"Oh, the farmer comes to town
   With his wagon broken down,
   But the farmer is the man who feeds them all.
   If you'll only look and see,
   I think you will agree
   That the farmer is the man who feeds them all.

"The farmer is the man,
   The farmer is the man,
   Lives on credit till the fall;
   Then they take him by the hand
   And they lead him from the land,
   And the merchant is the man who gets it all."

In 1890 the United States census announced that the frontier had disappeared. There was no more first-rate farm land that could be given away. People kept coming anyway. Land was ripped up that never should have been farmed at all.

President Johnson had said that it would take six hundred years for people to take over all the usable land in the public domain. Most of it had been taken over in less than a hundred years. Never in all of history had land been changed so fast from wilderness to a place where people lived as farmers or cattlemen or built their towns, waiting for more people to come.

Homesteading has not ended entirely, even now. The new frontier is our forty-ninth state, Alaska. In the spring of 1959 the Michigan '59ers, thirty-seven of them, set out from Detroit for Alaska, where they had been promised free farm land by the United States government. They settled in a forest wilderness across a mile-wide river from a town called Talkeetna, a hundred miles north of Anchorage. There they have been hacking out their farms by cutting down trees and digging out their roots with tractors and bulldozers. Trees have been used for building log houses.

Maybe the early pioneers had a harder time clearing the land, without tractors or bulldozers. But the use of a bulldozer costs plenty, and homesteading in Alaska is hard.

Soil there is rich, once you can get at it. The growing season is short, but summer days are eighteen hours long, so crops grow fast. The future may be good in Alaska for the Michigan '59ers, but some farms won't really pay for ten years.

Meanwhile, the nearest stores and the railroad are across the wild river. There is no bridge. In winter, people can walk across on the ice. In summer, the only way is by plane.

More than half of the Michigan '59ers have not stayed on their homesteads. Some have homesteaded elsewhere. Some have found jobs in the nearest city, Anchorage. Those who stayed think they are going to make out all right. They like being pioneers on their own land. Maybe they will never get rich there, but they are living the way they like to live, planning their own lives, close to nature every day of the year.

There had been other attempts to set up colonies of homesteaders in Alaska. For thirty years this was unsuccessful. Then the Matanuska Valley Colonization Project was established in 1935. This project is northeast of Anchorage and not very far from Talkeetna. Matanuska Valley has thrived. If they can stick it out, the Michigan '59ers will have a chance to thrive, too.

After all, where else in this country can people be pioneers today?

13: Oklahoma

Probably no land in the world has ever been settled as fast as was the Territory of Oklahoma. In a few short years, miles of earth were plowed and planted, towns were built, railway tracks were laid. Not long after that, factories were producing goods, newspapers were being printed, theaters entertained the people. All this was accomplished as white people settled on Indian land which had never before been turned by a plow. Before this time, in any other place, such development would have taken hundreds of years.

This quick settlement could not have been accomplished without the fertility of the rich red soil of Oklahoma. It could also not have been done without the purchase of many things from more settled areas outside the Territory, or without the help of the United States government.

At the beginning of 1889, Oklahoma was Indian Territory. The name Oklahoma itself means Home of the Red Man in the Choctaw tongue.

Many of the Indians belonging to the Five Civilized Tribes were living in Oklahoma, not because this had been the home of their ancestors, not because they chose to, but because the United States government had driven them there by force.

These Five Civilized Tribes were the Cherokees, Choctaws, Chickasaws, Creeks, and Seminoles. They had lived in the southeastern part of this country and were really more civilized than the other Indians of the East. The Cherokees were peaceful people, industrious, friendly to the whites, with a government not unlike the white man's. One of their great men, Sequoya, invented a useful alphabet which made it possible for the Cherokees to read and write.

For a number of years the Cherokees were allowed to keep their land as an independent nation within the boundaries of Georgia. But white men wanted that land. They kept pestering the United States government about it.

In 1828 Congress passed the Indian Removal Act. All the eastern tribes were to be driven to some place west of the Mississippi River. The Cherokees refused to go. They appealed to the government, which had guaranteed to them the possession of their lands by treaty. It was no use. In 1838 most of the Cherokees began their long trek West, driven by the United States Army like cattle across hundreds of miles of plains. Thousands died before they reached Oklahoma.

That is how the Cherokees, with the four other Civilized Tribes, were settled in Oklahoma before 1889. As in their eastern home, all the land was held by the tribe for the use of everyone. No individual could own any of it.

But the Oklahoma land was fertile. White people wanted that, too. Already it began to look as if there might not be enough land for settlement farther north and west. People kept after the government, insisting that the Indian Territory should be opened up to settlement. These people were called Boomers. They were constantly invading Indian land and being thrown out by United States soldiers. They intended to go in one day and stay.

The Boomers won out.

First, the government decided that the Indians ought to own land the way white people did. The head of each family was given 160 acres of good land. Each family was expected to live on and off just its own piece of land. The Indians resisted, but they had little choice. This kind of land owner-ship broke up tribal customs and destroyed the Indians' gov-ernment. To them this system of ownership seemed entirely wrong.

By this system, too, there was land left over. Maybe the Indians didn't need all that territory, after all. And so the Indian Territory was opened up for settlement, all at once, in an extraordinary land rush at exactly noon on April 22, 1889.

Some people crept in and staked their claims beforehand. They were called Sooners.

Thousands of people gathered in the neighboring states in March and April, waiting for their chance to cross the border and claim their acres. These were land-hungry people who had waited ten years for their hunger to be satisfied.

They crowded and cursed and fought for places near the line. The hot sun blazed down on them. As the time ap-proached, the roar of voices grew louder.

At last, it was twelve o'clock. The soldiers fired into the air. This was the signal for the start of the Run. But the clamor of the thousands of people made so much noise that not a single one of them could hear the crack of the muskets. Still, they knew it was time; they could see the smoke of the guns.

Over the line they swept, and across the prairie, people on foot and on horseback, in buggies and in wagons, all look-ing for a piece of land they could call their own without paying a cent.

Through most of history, it has taken as much as a hundred years for people to settle a new land and make it livable. Oklahoma was settled almost overnight.

On that one day at least twelve thousand, perhaps as many as forty thousand, people crossed the border into Oklahoma. These were mostly heads of families; women and children came later. A few weeks after the great land rush, the population of Oklahoma was about sixty thousand.

All the crops failed the next year. Nothing could grow. For the first time, but not the last, Oklahoma was declared a disaster area by the United States government. Congress voted emergency aid.

Wind blew topsoil off dry land in western Oklahoma. The short grass had been turned wrong side up. No one could foresee what would happen when this loose earth began to blow in the wind.

The Oklahomans who settled on Indian land in 1889 must have supposed that they were starting farms that would last for generations. These farms should belong to their children and their children's children.

It didn't always work out that way. On some of the most easily plowed land, it was only a generation before the soil died beneath the farmer's feet. On others, it took a little longer.

Why? Drought wasn't anything a farmer could help. But he *could* help what he did about it. These farmers knew the same farming methods that had been used in western Europe, as well as in the eastern part of North America. They were the wrong methods for the plains. Here were soils rich in plant foods which looked and felt like the best possible soil for growing grain. But the climate was not like that of Europe at all. In northwestern Europe, there is almost always plenty of rain. In our Middle West, there is not even half as much as in Europe. Grass had survived on the plains for centuries by holding every drop of rain in the vast sponge of its roots. Wind could not blow away soil held tight by those roots.

There would have to be a different way of farming on the plains.

Less than forty-five years after the great land rush in Oklahoma, in 1933, people all along the eastern coast of this country felt a great shadow hiding the brightness of the day. The Weather Bureau had predicted fair weather. Well, this wasn't very fair weather. People looked up. Overhead hung a strange dark cloud. It didn't look like an ordinary cloud. It seemed to be reddish brown instead of gray. People shivered uneasily. They didn't like the looks of that cloud. There was something uncanny about it.

Five hundred miles out to sea, a ship on the Atlantic Ocean saw a big dark cloud approaching. The barometer had predicted fair weather. What was this?

It was the same red-brown cloud people had seen along the eastern coast, blown out to sea by strong winds from the west.

That whole cloud consisted of good topsoil from dry farms in Oklahoma and other parts of the Great Plains. When the wind died down, this soil settled down on streets, on rooftops and fields in the East or fell quietly into the ocean. It takes nature, under the most favorable conditions, two hundred to a thousand years, or even more, to build a single inch of topsoil from the materials in the soil beneath the surface. Man can destroy that same inch of topsoil in less than a year.

None of the red-brown topsoil that blew East in a dark

cloud on that day in 1933 would ever find its way back to the plains from which it came. It was gone forever.

People began to see what was happening. Now, not just a few but many people began to ask what was wrong with the land.

And this dark cloud was only a beginning.

14: The Dust Bowl

In 1930 the weather was pretty dry all over this country. In 1931 it was even worse on the Great Plains. In 1932 it did rain a little, but nowhere enough.

In 1933, on November 11, came the first of the terrible black blizzards. Clouds of topsoil blew off the Great Plains. In the daytime, it was darker than night. People lost their way when they were only a hundred yards from home. Strange shapes were dimly seen through the darkness. These might be lost sheep. A sudden bump from something blowing out of nowhere was tumbleweed in the wind.

The next day, the whole sky was dark over Chicago. Topsoil sifted down onto the streets, onto the roofs, into Lake Michigan.

The spring of 1934 brought wind, and no rain. There were more clouds of dust. In New York City, on what should have been a bright day, dust shut out the sun for five hours.

On the Great Plains, rivers had dried up and left earth as hard as cement and full of cracks.

People tied handkerchiefs around their faces when the dust clouds came. Dust got into their mouths anyway, into their noses and their eyes. They tried to rub it out of their eyes. They sneezed it out of their noses. People had dust even in their ears. Everyone had a sore throat.

If you reached in your pocket, dust was there. Your back itched with having dust blown down your neck. When you opened a book, there was dust between the pages.

Many people gave up and left. Their houses stood empty and full of dust. Other people tried to stick it out. They had been so sure that farming on the Great Plains was a good way to live. They hung wet blankets over their doors and windows. Dust blew in anyway.

Hopefully, some people planted wheat or cotton. They irrigated it if they could. A few green shoots came up. But it didn't rain. Wind blew dust over the shoots.

People tried to joke about their troubles. One farmer remarked that his farm had taken a trip north. But it would be back next week. He could plow it then. The poet Archibald MacLeish spoke for the people in *Land of the Free:*

> "All we know for sure—the land's going out from us:
> Blown out by the dry wind in the wheat:
> Blown clean to the arrow-heads under the centuries:
> Blown to the stony clay . . .
>   and we get wondering:
> We wonder if the liberty was land."

The southern Great Plains, where Kansas, Oklahoma, Texas, New Mexico, and Colorado come together, was called the Dust Bowl. It was dry there until 1938; seven years of blowing topsoil.

Good rains came again. On the Great Plains they always do. But very few farmers would ever again take these rains for granted. It was wise to be ready for the years when it didn't rain.

Four hundred years before, a Spanish explorer on the Great Plains had found a sea of waving grass reaching to the horizon and beyond. If he had seen the same plains in the 1930s, he would not have thought it was the same place.

The situation looked almost hopeless. No one could make it rain—at least, not enough to help. No one could ever put the blown topsoil back again. What was the use of staying on a farm where you couldn't ever be sure of growing a crop?

Some people hung on, hoping. Some stayed because they didn't know where else to go. They couldn't sell their farms; no one wanted them. If they couldn't sell, what would they use for money?

One family that stayed was the Anderson family, on the edge of the Great Plains. All their neighbors had gone. They were getting ready to go, too, one April, when Mr. Anderson and his son went to a meeting in the nearest town. At the meeting, experts from the Soil Conservation Service of the United States Department of Agriculture were going to talk about putting in crops.

"Putting in crops?" said Mr. Anderson. "I guess I know how to put 'em in. What I need to know is how to keep 'em there."

Mr. Anderson and his son listened while soil technicians told them about stopping wind erosion and beating the drought. Maybe there were ways of doing it, after all.

The next day, the soil technicians came out to the Anderson farm to look things over. They were going to tell the Andersons whether they could do something about their farm, or whether they should just give up and clear out.

The soil conservation experts urged the Andersons to stay. Their farm might still be good for growing crops, if they would use it right. This was the best news that family had heard in years.

Here is what the Andersons did, after the soil experts had shown them how:

They built terraces on their sloping fields, almost level

shelves of land that would hold the rain—when it did rain. They hadn't supposed they needed terraces. Their fields weren't hilly. But they sloped just enough for water and loose topsoil to run down when it rained. This kind of washing off of soil is called sheet erosion.

The next month, the Andersons plowed their terraced fields, not up and down as they used to do, but following the terraces around the contour or curve of the slopes. Then they planted crops that didn't need much water but would add some good plant food and organic matter to the soil.

There was a little rain that spring. Not enough to help, Mr. Anderson thought. But what rain there was stayed on the terraces and soaked into the ground.

For the first time in four years, the Andersons looked out on green fields. The harvest was fair. They left the roots of the plants in the ground, and stalks standing, to hold down the earth.

The land didn't blow in the winter winds, or in the early spring. Soil was in pretty good condition for spring planting.

The harvest that year was better. By the third year, the Andersons' land had recovered enough so they could grow wheat again.

There were wide green fields that spring on their farm. The Andersons weren't going to clear out. They had learned how to make a good living right there on the land, if it would rain at least a little every year.

The Andersons' land was worth saving, first of all, because it was land that had always been suitable for farming. If it had been good only for pasture, the technicians from the Soil Conservation Service would have advised the Andersons to plant grass that needs little moisture and pasture cattle on it. Much of the land on the plains is good only for pastures.

If there had been even less rain than the Andersons had,

they would have had to irrigate their land, if they could, by bringing in water from somewhere, somehow.

If the land had been too worn out to be good for farming, or maybe even for pasturing, or if too much of the fertile topsoil had blown off, the Andersons would have been advised to leave. There is nothing gained when beaten people struggle year after year to make a meager living from soil that will always be too poor to feed them well and provide enough income to live on decently.

The Soil Conservation Service was established in the United States Department of Agriculture in 1935, to help farmers like Mr. Anderson in their use of the land. You will read more about this in a later chapter.

All over this country, farmers have been learning how to take care of their soil. If enough of them learn, the soil of America can still be saved.

15: What Had Happened to the Land?

The Dust Bowl happened in the 1930s. The soil that blew off the Great Plains during those years was dry enough to blow partly because there was too little rain. But most of the soil would have stayed where it belonged if much of the grassland that wasn't good for cultivation had not been plowed up and laid bare by eager farmers. It took a good many years of breaking up and plowing the plains before winds could blow up enough dry soil to shut out the light of the sun.

Homesteading was popular from the time of the Homestead Act in 1862 to about the end of the century. The Desert Land Act of 1877 gave 640 acres of dry land to a hopeful farmer or cattleman, if he thought he could irrigate it somehow.

The government gave 158 million acres to the railroads, with the timber above and the coal and ore beneath.

With the railroad crossing the plains, it was no longer so hard to be a homesteader. A man could take his family along and be sure they would get there safe and well. The railroads put on fantastic advertising campaigns. Every passenger meant a ticket sold.

It sounded so easy. It wasn't too hard for those who got good land, but some got poor land.

There were more and more people in this country. By 1875 there were forty-four and a half million mouths to feed. That was twenty-one and a half million more than in 1850. In 1900 there were seventy-six million.

More land was plowed to feed all these people. More wheat was sowed and harvested. There was hardly enough. Men mined the land for corn and wheat and cotton, just as they mined it for iron and gold and copper.

Land wore out. It still didn't seem to matter. There was more land farther west. People were a little drunk with the thought of all the wealth that was theirs.

There were many who used the land only to make money. There were those, too, who loved the land and used it well.

People thought the soil would last forever. A bulletin of the United States Department of Agriculture, published in 1909, stated that "the soil is the one resource that cannot be exhausted; that cannot be used up."

It wasn't many years before the Department itself admitted that it was completely wrong.

Homesteading subsided a little in the early 1900s. When the Three-Year Homestead Act was passed, the number of homesteaders doubled.

Then, in 1914, came World War I. The war wasn't fought on our land. But in Europe, not counting Russia, fifty million acres of farm land were useless after the war. No one could grow wheat or anything else on this land until it was cleaned up and in good condition again.

United States farmers supplied the wheat that Europe couldn't grow. People would have starved by thousands if they had not had our wheat.

Growing this wheat meant digging up more of the Great Plains, plowing up grassy hills, trying to farm areas that had always been pretty dry.

This was in the 1920s. And it was after that, in the 1930s, that the bad dust storms started.

When European farmers had brought much of their land back into good condition, Europe didn't need so much of our wheat. Prices fell. Many farmers lost their farms.

Much land that had been used for wheat was left unused. The dust blew and blew.

The eager settlers of Oklahoma may have thought they were founding a new farming civilization that would last as long as Egypt. But thousands of their grandchildren, sometimes even their children, couldn't make a living on that land at all. They trekked West from their ruined farms, their dead soil, with dust of their own making on their faces. These were the Okies, tired and bewildered people traveling with whatever they could take with them, a few mattresses to sleep on, worn-out cooking pots, clothes that were ragged and covered with the dry dust of the earth from which they came.

The Okies went west to earn what money they could picking fruit in California. There was plenty of fruit growing there, while the season lasted. For a long time, the Okies hadn't been able to grow enough to keep even themselves alive, on their own dry and blowing land.

This was the time when the Farm Security Administration, a government agency that was trying to help the farmers in trouble, put out a striking documentary film called *The Plow That Broke the Plains*. The story of the plains was told in simple and moving language by Pare Lorentz. The music composed by Virgil Thompson for the film gives us a feeling for the vastness of the plains and the folklore of the people who live there.

It begins:

"This is a record of the land. . . .
A high, treeless continent,
Without rivers, without streams . . .
A country of high winds, and sun . . .
and little rain . . ."

And it ends:

"The sun and the winds wrote the most tragic chapter
in American agriculture."

Later, John Steinbeck was to write his great novel, *The Grapes of Wrath*, about the Okies, and Twentieth Century-Fox made it into a movie. Tom Joad in the book became a symbol of all the Okies who ever traveled the long road west away from dust and starvation.

It is easy to blame the Okies, or their fathers and grandfathers, for what they did to the land. But they were not the only ones. Millions of people, not all of them farmers, have had to find out that you can't ignore the laws of nature without bringing disaster on yourself and the millions of other people who depend on the land. Not knowing this, or not caring, is no excuse.

16: Land in the South

It was easy, in the days of the Dust Bowl, to think that the Great Plains was the only part of this country that had real problems with its land. But this wasn't so. No part of this country is entirely without land problems. The southeastern part has had more than its share.

In the Dust Bowl, wind blowing topsoil up into clouds had become the worst problem. In the South, which means the southeastern part of this country, the main problem was rain washing soil off unprotected land. This made little channels in the earth. These in time became big gullies.

Misuse of the land became a problem almost as soon as the South was settled. The careless farming methods of many southern farmers went west with those who settled on the prairie and the Great Plains. If these farmers, and their fathers and grandfathers, had known how to take good care of the land in the South, they might have done better in the West.

Land in the South had been used for growing tobacco or cotton, year after year, without any rest in between. There was not much nourishment for growing plants left in the soil. Fertilizer did not seem to help as much as it should. Boll weevils ate much of the cotton.

Both tobacco and cotton are clean-tilled crops. That is, they are grown in rows with nothing in between the rows. Wherever these rows were planted straight up and down the slope, rain washed off the soil between rows. Good topsoil muddied the streams and ran down them to the ocean.

Sometimes fields that were worn out were just left empty. Before the weeds could put their roots down deep enough to hold the earth, tons of it were washing away. Not all weeds are good for holding the soil, in any case.

Stewart County, Georgia, is almost an exhibition place for gullies, fifty thousand acres of them. The soil there used to be fertile red earth. It still is red on top, wherever the top part is left.

The hills in Stewart County were used for growing crops without any protection in the bare places. And the red earth washed off, down to yellow subsoil and brown clay, every rainstorm digging deeper into the earth.

On one farm, a gully was formed just by the dripping of rain off a barn roof. The drip made a little furrow in the bare earth at first, then a bigger channel where the water ran downhill. Finally it became a deep gully that had gouged out more than three thousand acres of land. This gully even had a name, Providence Cave. Cave because the sides might cave in any minute. Providence because it was near Providence Church.

In the 1930s, writer Stuart Chase went to see this gully. He looked down into it. This is how he described it in his book, *Rich Land, Poor Land:*

"The chasm was awful and beautiful. The earth strata changed from red to yellow to brown, mauve, lavender, jade, ocher, orange and chalk white. . . . Along the banks, trees were in all stages of collapse—some just ready to plunge downward, some holding on by their roots with might and main, some leaning crazily outward. At the bottom, a few small pine trees were alive and growing. Sometimes one lived with its red sod about it halfway down the slope where it had fallen. There was no water at the bottom. When the rains came, soil and water rushed off through a vent to the Chattahoochee River."

Much work has been done, since the 1930s, to stop soil erosion in the South. Vines such as kudzu have been planted on the sides of gullies. These vines put down tight roots which hold the earth. They spread over the ground, putting down more and more roots.

Gullies have been stopped. But once a gully is made, it is almost impossible to fill it up. It will never be good farm land again. And that includes fifty thousand acres in Stewart County.

There were many reasons for neglect of the land in the South. In the beginning, of course, people were careless with the land because there seemed to be so much of it. Then, there was the need to make money from it quickly, first to pay the trading companies which had sent settlers to the New World, and then for the prosperity of the settlers themselves.

To many people, all over the country, taking care of the land has seemed just too expensive. At the moment, it may be expensive. But in the long run, the losses from careless farming are too great even to imagine.

There were other factors that helped spoil land in the South. Most landowners had big plantations, and the work on the land was done by slaves. The owners were seldom close to the land. Many of them did not care how the land was used. Often they did not care what happened to the slaves, either, so long as the crops grew and brought a good price.

Too often in the history of the world, people have been exploited, that is, used for the profit of other people, as the slaves were in the South. When this has happened, the land has usually been exploited, too. People who are willing to use other human beings for their own profit are not apt to care what happens to the land.

After the Civil War, the situation in the South changed drastically. Without slaves, most plantation owners could not make their farming pay. Some went West. Many gave up farming and moved to the cities, leaving behind them acres of eroding land. Some sold their land.

A different system of land use grew up, sharecropping. The workers who were left on the land had to live somehow. So the owners divided the land into one-man farms and rented them to tenants. Rent was usually a share of the crops raised.

This may seem like a fair system, but it didn't usually work out that way. The land remained poor. The tenant hardly ever had enough, after giving the landlord his share, to make a decent living for himself and his family.

The tenant had to buy fertilizer, to make the land grow anything at all. The landlord wanted at least a certain amount each year. Many sharecroppers had to plant cotton right up to their own front doors, in order to grow enough. There wasn't any room for a little vegetable garden for the family. The children had to work in the fields. Even so, it was hard to feed them all. No matter how hard they worked, things never seemed to get any better.

The landlord did all right. He made money. But the sharecropper seldom had a chance to improve his way of living. He was something like the peasant in the Middle Ages. Of course, he could move to another farm. Then he would be sharing crops from a different piece of land. It wasn't likely to make any difference. And he wasn't trained for any other kind of work.

If a farmer tried to practice conservation on his rented farm, he might even find that the landlord didn't like it. The landlord might decide that the farmer was acting too much as if he owned the place.

This kind of land ownership and use is not likely to be good for the land. The absentee landlord often has no love for it. The tenant sometimes cannot use it well even if he wants to. Much of the time he doesn't want to. The land isn't his.

The time has come when people who do not care about the land must not be allowed to ruin it for the people who will have to make their living from it in the future.

The South has suffered more from water erosion than any other part of the country. Southern farmers have been to blame. Perhaps most of them did not know what they were doing to the land. Some of them didn't care. Those yawning gullies in Stewart County were all man-made.

But the pattern of land use in the South has been changing. Southern soils were rich, with many of the minerals that plants need for growth, and much can be made fertile again. The South is more prosperous now than it was after the Civil War. Industries have helped. But the land, too, is being reclaimed. Some of the methods that are being used date back to the first farmer who ever dug manure into his soil. Others are the best that modern science has been able to develop. This soil can become a living thing again, rich with organic materials.

Much has been learned, in this country and all over the world, about the care of the soil that grows our food. There is a new applied science, soil conservation, which includes everything that can be done to keep the soil on this earth in good condition for the use of plants, animals, and people. An understanding of soil conservation has become a necessary part of good farming.

17: The Father of Soil Conservation

We have seen that, almost from the time the first white man dug up the earth on this continent for his garden, the American earth has been wasted and worn out, blown away and washed away, at a rate never heard of in the world before. Wasn't anything being done about this at all?

At first, very little was done. There were, to be sure, a few people who saw what was happening: George Washington took good care of his land; Thomas Jefferson plowed his fields around the slopes, instead of straight up and down. There were other experts who wrote about rotating crops and caring for the soil. But these ideas were not popular. On rectangular pieces of land, straight plowing seemed to fit better than curving lines, and farmers thought it looked better.

Aside from the few people here and there who took good care of the land, there were whole groups of people who did better than others. Settlers who came from parts of Europe where good ways of farming were well established brought those methods with them and adapted them to the soil they found here. These were the Germans, the Dutch, the Swedes, and others, who settled in Pennsylvania, Delaware, and Maryland.

Before the Civil War, the Confederate leader Edmund Ruffin pointed out that the South was becoming poorer mostly because the soil was wearing out. If this had not been so, he said, more people would have stayed in the South, instead of going West.

Ruffin energetically busied himself with reviving southern agriculture. He recommended fertilization of the soil and control of erosion. He found that peas were a good crop for stopping water erosion. One thing he tried was planting various crops in a six-year rotation system, a different crop each year, each preparing the soil for the next one.

Ruffin worked hard at this. He tried out his own ideas and other people's ideas, thoroughly. Then he wrote about his results.

Most farmers just laughed. Newfangled nonsense, they said. But some tried Ruffin's ideas. His methods worked very well, in the limited areas where they were tried.

Then came the Civil War and the death of Ruffin. No one knows how much more land in the South might have been saved if Ruffin could have continued his work.

All this time, soil conservation as an applied science did not exist. But it was on the way. The man most responsible for this was Hugh Hammond Bennett, often called Big Hugh, the father of soil conservation.

Hugh Bennett first became interested in saving the soil when he was ten years old. Topsoil was washing off the land pretty badly on the Bennett family farm in North Carolina. Hugh's father had decided to try terracing. The boy's job was marking off the lines for the plows to follow in making the terraces. It was hard work, and he wanted to know why they were going to all that trouble.

His father's answer stuck in the boy's mind: "To keep the

land from washing away!" Hugh kept wondering. He couldn't have known it then, but his life work was going to be helping to keep the land in this country from washing and blowing away.

Bennett's first job was doing a soil survey for the Bureau of Soils of the United States Department of Agriculture in 1903. This took him all over the country. He talked with farmers everywhere and studied their land by walking over it with them. There wasn't anyone in the country who knew the land better than Hugh Bennett, and he was getting a pretty good idea of what was wrong with it. Already he was thinking about what could be done to keep the soil where it belonged and keep it fertile.

Saving the soil was going to take a lot of hard work by a lot of people, and education. Bennett found that even the farmers didn't always understand what was happening to their land. They hated gullies. All they had to do was to look at a yawning gully to hate it. But most of them didn't know a thing about sheet erosion, the washing away of great sheets of soil, usually on land that doesn't slope much. It isn't easy to see sheet erosion. It happens all over the land, a little at a time. Gullies are much more dramatic.

Hugh Bennett saw the sheet erosion that was going on all over this country, and he determined to do something about it. He was a good talker. People listened, and thought about what he was saying. In those days, as we have seen, some of the soil experts had pretty mistaken ideas about the soil. They thought it couldn't really be destroyed. Hugh Bennett said it could be destroyed and that this was just what was happening.

Some of the experts said, too, that the only thing that took fertility away from the soil was growing crops on it until it was worn out. Bennett was going to prove that this wasn't so. Erosion could do the same thing by taking off the fertile topsoil.

It wasn't going to be enough to talk with individual farmers. There were too many of them, and most of them didn't want to change their ways. Bennett talked with congressional committees and agencies. He bothered people in the Department of Agriculture. Soil was a problem the government was going to have to do something about.

One time, Bennett wanted to show some congressmen how soil absorbed water. He spread a bath towel on a tilted board and poured water on it from a pitcher. The towel absorbed all the water, just as soil would. Then he took the towel away and poured water on the bare board. It all ran off. This, he explained, is what happens on hard land with nothing growing on it.

Progress was slow. It was not until 1929 that the government began a thorough study of soil erosion. That year the first erosion-control experiment station was set up at Guthrie, Oklahoma. Others were started soon after.

Soil erosion was becoming a national emergency. In 1933 the government set up the Soil Erosion Service, with Hugh Bennett as director. This was the first agency ever set up for the control of erosion in the history of the world.

At last, something was getting done. Hugh Bennett was going to make sure that still more was done.

In 1935 he testified before a committee in favor of an important soil conservation bill. He talked and he talked. He gave the senators all the facts and figures he could think of. He talked about a dust storm that had almost blotted out the sun right in the city of Washington the year before. There had been two more this year. Each storm had blown off the land tons of fertile soil, about enough to make 150 thousand acres of land twelve inches deep.

What Bennett didn't tell the senators was that he was waiting, right that minute, for another dust cloud to arrive. He knew it was coming. He had weather reports that told him so. But he wished that cloud would hurry up! He was getting tired of talking.

Then one of the senators said, "It's getting dark. Maybe it's going to rain."

Another gave a guess. "Maybe it's dust."

Bennett nodded his head. "Senator, it does look like dust."

They looked out the window. The dust storm Hugh Bennett had known was coming rolled in over the city. The sun disappeared. All the sky was coppery brown. The air was full of dust, gritty soil blown from the Great Plains.

Just then a page boy hurried in and handed a telegram to one of the senators from a friend in Oklahoma City: "Worst of all desert storms now raging in this city. Street lights are on. You can't see the length of a block."

Nobody was surprised. Everyone could see the Oklahoma dirt, and Texas dirt, right outside the window. It seeped in, and they could grind it between their teeth.

Nobody doubted any more that something would have to be done. Congress passed the National Soil Conservation Act creating the Soil Conservation Service as an agency of the United States Department of Agriculture. The earlier Soil Erosion Service had been in the Department of the Interior. Hugh Bennett was chief of the new agency.

The Soil Conservation Service has gone on spreading the knowledge of how to keep our topsoil where it belongs, helping farmers to take care of their land, and, more important, showing them that it pays.

Hugh Bennett always knew that his plans for soil conservation would have to *work*. Plans were made carefully and scientifically. There were still plenty of people, not all

Using a land capability map.

Left: poor soil from a cultivated field.
Right: rich crumbly soil from an undisturbed fence row
only 25 feet away.

Irrigation in contour furrows, California.

Strip cropping in Dutchess County, New York.

A seed drill in action on a field in India.

Terraces built on slopes in northeastern China.

Marking trees to be cut down in a forest, Oklahoma.

Continuing life on the forest floor, Washington.

of them farmers, who said that the whole thing was nonsense. Soil conservation could never recover from the disaster of a major plan that didn't work.

Hugh Bennett's plans did work. People came from all over the world to consult him about the management of the soil in their own countries. Many nations have established soil conservation departments like ours. The Food and Agricultural Organization of the United Nations has made studies and recommendations for soil conservation all over the world. The Crow Indians adopted Hugh Bennett, because he helped save their hunting grounds.

The work is not finished. Hugh Bennett retired from his work with the Soil Conservation Service in 1952. He died in 1960. It is no longer hard to convince most people that soil conservation is important. But it is still a big job to get the work done, everywhere, on big farms and little farms. People have to learn to care.

Hugh Bennett gave some idea of the size of the problem when he said that if the soil lost every year in the United States by erosion were put in ordinary railroad gondola cars, it would fill a train reaching four times around the earth at the equator.

The whole world now has only about four billion acres of land that can be used for growing food and other crops. Not all of this is good land. Maybe four billion acres seems a lot. In a world the size of ours, with our increasing billions of people, it may not be enough.

18: The Soil Conservation Service

"Each acre of land must be used according to its individual capability and treated according to its needs," Hugh Hammond Bennett said.

He knew that farmers like to do things themselves. They like to do things their own way, too, as long as they can. So when the men in the Soil Conservation Service set out to help farmers take better care of the land, they didn't just order them to do this or that, or tell them the government had decided that a certain way of farming was right for their land. Instead, the responsibility for soil conservation programs was given to local communities. No conservation program was likely to succeed unless the farmers themselves wanted it and were willing to cooperate with other farmers in carrying it out.

Here is how local soil conservation work is done. A Soil Conservation District is set up for a given area, after local farmers have voted for it. Usually the area is a county or the watershed of a river. Each state has laws governing the work of Soil Conservation Districts. State conservation committees help the Districts with such detail as setting boundaries and dividing up the work.

114

The District then often divides its cooperating farmers into small workable groups. These groups plan their work and help one another to apply conservation principles to their land.

This is where the Soil Conservation Service itself comes in. Their experts help farmers lay out the fields for contour plowing and strip crops. They make plans for terracing, where it is needed, designs for ponds and irrigation systems, and plans for control of gullies. Most farmers cannot do all this by themselves. It requires special knowledge and training.

Sometimes the Soil Conservation Service, in cooperation with the farmers and various interested organizations, will give a single farm a face-lifting, a demonstration of what can be done for the land. Careful planning is done beforehand. On the day of the demonstration, people come from miles around to watch. Experts from the Soil Conservation Service arrive. Bulldozers, tractors, and other farm machines roar into the farm. Only a run-down farm will do for this demonstration!

Fields are plowed, with furrows following the contours of the sloping earth. Terraces, like steps, are made on slopes that are too steep for contour plowing alone, but not too steep for growing crops. Terraces will hold the water and the soil when it rains.

If there is a brook, the demonstrators may build a little dam across it to make a farm pond. This will hold water even in driest weather.

No farmer could ever do all this to his farm in one day. It would take him years. But by watching for just one day he can get an idea of what can be done. He'll probably decide it's worth a try.

The men in the Soil Conservation Service know that their business is not just saving land but saving people, from poverty and despair and often from hunger. Care of the land can mean that much to people.

Let's see how the Soil Conservation Service can help an individual farmer. In the 1940s, Ted Jackson lived with his wife and six children in a three-room house that needed painting, on a 120-acre farm in the South. Rent was forty dollars a year. Jackson paid it when he made that much. His cash crop was cotton. Sometimes he didn't make more than thirty dollars on cotton. Then he'd be behind on his rent, with nothing to spend on himself and his family.

The Jacksons lived crowded into their small house. Not enough beds. Rough boxes to sit on. A roof that leaked when it rained.

Supper might be black-eyed peas cooked with fatback, bread and molasses, peanuts grown on the place. No fresh meat, no green vegetables, no fruit. Milk only sometimes.

Jackson was using thirty of the acres on his farm, mostly for growing cotton. Most of those thirty acres shouldn't have been used for cotton. This is hilly country. All over the county in which Jackson lived there were gullies so big you could drop a house into them. Jackson himself didn't have any gullies that big—yet.

Jackson grew cotton next to his house where the land sloped down to a stream. Gullies had started there.

He grew corn for his family on a pretty steep hillside, with the rows running straight up and down the hill. When it rained, topsoil from the hill ran just one way—down. The top of the hill was half gone. Corn was poor and scraggly. Half of it didn't even grow ears. Peanuts and black-eyed peas did a little better, near the brook.

Jackson knew what the trouble was. He knew he was trying to grow crops on thin subsoil, worn-out soil, he called it.

He knew that much. But he didn't know what to do about it. He guessed he'd have to clear a big patch of trees off one side of the hill and plow that up. Next year he'd have to plow up some other patch of trees. Pretty soon the whole farm would be worn out.

The county agriculture agent had talked with Jackson. He had told him he shouldn't plant corn on such a steep hill. But Jackson said he had to have the corn close enough to his house so he could take care of it. He and his sons had about all they could do to keep things going as it was. Cotton came first. Cotton was what paid the rent—or almost did.

The agent had said the cotton wasn't planted right, either. Well, what could a man do?

When the farmers in Jackson's county organized a Soil Conservation District, Jackson wasn't enthusiastic. At least, not at first. He was afraid conservation farming would cost him money. But he became a District cooperator, because all the other farmers did. It wouldn't hurt to give it a try.

First the District worked out a conservation program and work plan for the whole area. The Soil Conservation Service helped with this. Individual farmers agreed to cooperate.

This is always the first step. Next is the making of individual farm plans. With these plans, farmers learn how to practice conservation on their own farms. The Soil Conservation Service sends in experts on soil and water to help with the plans. Often, farmers work together in carrying them out. Farmers have to put a good deal of their own time, muscle, and equipment into this work. There are two reasons for this: the job gets done, and the farmers value it because they have put so much effort into it themselves.

Let's see what happened to Ted Jackson's farm, after he

became a cooperator with the local Soil Conservation District. First of all, he found out that anything he could do to improve the land was all right with the owner. He could even buy the farm if he could get together enough money.

Scientists from the Soil Conservation Service made a study of Jackson's land and called it a land-use capability survey. They walked over his land and studied the soil, the slopes, how the water drained off, the condition of the land, and what it was being used for.

All this information was then put on a land-use map, with various colors and patterns to show the slopes and the kind of land in each area.

The Soil Conservation Service puts land into eight broad classes, according to whether it is good for cultivation, good for limited use, or for wildlife.

When Jackson's map was finished, it looked very gay, with different colors all over it in patches. Each color meant a specific class of land. Jackson looked for green. That was Class I land, good for cultivation with ordinary farming methods. Nearly level and easy to work. Jackson had just two small patches of green. That was better than none at all. Very few farms had much Class I land.

Pink on the map was Class III, pretty good land which can be cultivated if it is given such treatment as terracing, strip cropping, and crop rotation. Jackson had quite a bit of that.

He found that his eroded cornfield on the slope was colored blue on the map: Class IV land. Suited to pasture and hay but not good for continuous cultivation.

Much of Jackson's land was marked in salmon color: Class V, not suitable for cultivation at all. All right for grazing or forestry.

Any land-use map is just a beginning. The plan for Jackson's farm had to include, too, a survey of how many people there were in the family, how many of them could help with farm work, how much money Jackson made, and so on. Sociologists and other experts made this survey. After all, conservation is not just for the land. Conservation is for people. Poor soil means poor people.

The weather in that area was studied, too. How much rain, how hard it rained. Water experts have even studied the effect of raindrops on the land. Gentle rains drop gently on uncovered earth, disturbing it only a little. Big fast drops land so hard that the earth is packed down and the water can't sink in fast enough. There was plenty of heavy rain in Jackson's part of the country.

All these surveys were used by experts in making Ted Jackson's farm plan. This plan would tell him what he could really do with his land.

One thing was certain. The way he'd been doing things so far was wrong. He shouldn't grow any more corn and cotton on the slopes. Both of these are clean-tilled crops, with nothing growing between the rows. Land where they grow should be nearly level or made safe from erosion with contour plowing or strip cropping. Crops should be rotated, too.

Much of Jackson's land should be planted with trees before any more of it washed away. Some should be pasture. As soon as he had the money for it, Jackson bought a cow.

There was plenty of work ahead on Ted Jackson's farm. But now he was sure it would pay. His contact with the Soil Conservation Service had convinced him that he needn't just let the soil wash away around him.

He learned, too, how to build up his soil with manure

from his new cow, how to dig in green crops such as clover to enrich the earth. He learned to use fertilizer, not to try to make poor soil grow good crops when it can't, but to bring to his plants the minerals they needed and could not get from the worn-out soil.

Down in the lower pasture, Jackson's neighbors helped him build a dam across the brook, using plans the Soil Conservation Service men had helped him make. The dam was made with earth dug right out of the pasture where the pond was going to be. This dam held the water back, but no water went over it. Instead, the overflow, after the reservoir was filled, went over a cement spillway beside the dam.

The pond was almost ten feet deep, so it wouldn't get too full of weeds. Jackson was proud of it. He'd always have water now, in any weather. He even thought he'd put in a few fish, for his boys to catch and bring home for supper.

In time, Ted Jackson began to be prosperous. He didn't grow cotton at all now. It had already done too much damage to his land. But peanuts were a good cash crop, and he was going to try others. His corn was tall and full of plump ears. His pasture got better and better. After a while he bought more cows and set up a dairy business. He was saving money to buy the farm.

But that wasn't all. Ted Jackson had the satisfaction of being a good farmer. It was hard work, farming, but plowing good land and harvesting a good crop could satisfy a man as long as he lived. He wasn't forcing a poor crop from poor land now, he was working with nature, growing good plants in rich earth. This was going to be fertile soil long after he was through using it.

Ted Jackson didn't write down what he felt about the land. But another farmer, Ben Smith, wrote about it this way:

"Let me live close to the heart of things;
  Sun on my face; wind on the clover;
  Dew on the leaves where the wild bird sings;
  Smell of the earth that my plow turns over . . ."

This is what Ted Jackson might have said if he had been good at putting words together.

When you read about worn-out land, gullies, and dust storms, you may get the impression that the only parts of this country that need the Soil Conservation Service are in the South or on the Great Plains. But this is not so. As we have seen, there isn't any part of this country with no land problems at all. The Soil Conservation Service is ready to help anywhere.

Take Dutchess County in New York State, for example. The Soil Conservation District there has been active since 1942. It was started by a group of practical and progressive farmers who presented their ideas to local grange meetings and other groups. It wasn't long before there was enough interest to vote the Dutchess County Soil Conservation District into existence. Work started slowly, with contour strips laid out, ditches dug to carry off excess water, and brooks dammed up to make farm ponds. After a few years, however, the technicians from the Soil Conservation Service had more work than they could take care of. It still takes anywhere up to three years to get a job done by the Soil Conservation Service. They need more men to do the work.

Dutchess County was never a dust storm area. There were no gaping gullies like those in Georgia. Most of the farmers there thought they were doing pretty well. They had always planted their rows of corn straight up and down the slopes. A field of corn certainly looked nice planted that way. To be sure, they had seen some of the soil washing down the hills between the rows of corn after a storm, but they hadn't thought much about it. There ought to be plenty of soil.

Even so, it hadn't been too hard to persuade some of these farmers that they could do better. They hadn't made much money in recent years, and they'd begun to think something might be wrong with the way they were farming.

Other farmers have never been persuaded at all. They don't like anyone even suggesting that they might do a better job than they've been doing. It's nobody else's business anyhow, they say. They just want to be let alone. This might be all right if a farmer could just live alone on his farm, as if it were an island.

The farmers who became cooperators with the Dutchess County Soil Conservation District didn't know much about contour plowing or strip cropping. But they were willing to try them out and see what happened. If these methods had worked so well in other places, they might help here, too.

If you ask these farmers now, most of them will tell you they wouldn't think of farming any other way. Their soil stays where it belongs. They can grow more corn or grain on an acre than they'd ever thought they could. The top of each cultivated hill doesn't look washed off any more. It grows just as good crops as the bottom of the hill.

You can see the results of this farming if you drive through Dutchess County with your eyes open, especially on some of the lovely back roads. Wide strips of grass or oats curve around farm hillsides, alternating with strips of darker green corn. Most spectacular of all, in the fall, are the golden strips of corn stubble contrasting with green strips of grass all around a slope.

Here and there you will see a farm pond, made from a dammed-up brook, lush and green around the edges. You may see a family of ducks paddling serenely across, or even a pair of swans.

Occasionally, too, you may see rows of corn planted straight up and down a hill. Not everyone has learned.

The Soil Conservation District keeps trying. In December people from the District call on local farmers, asking them what they accomplished in conservation during the past year, and what they plan to do next year. No one has a chance to forget.

A good many of the farms in Dutchess County are owned by busy professional people who like to own land but do not have time to farm it themselves. Most of them can't even be there much of the time. Some of these people are well known on television, in the movies, and in other fields. They want their land farmed right, and they do their best to find a farm manager who will use the methods promoted by the Dutchess County Soil Conservation District. So we see that absentee owners are not always careless about their land. They may care a great deal about what happens to it.

All over this country, men in the Soil Conservation Service are helping farmers and landowners to take good care of their land, through their local Soil Conservation Districts. These men work hard, and they wish there were more of them to get the job done. It doesn't look as if this job would ever be finished.

19: Responsibility and the Land

A great deal has been done to keep the soil of the United States from washing away and blowing away, to keep our soil fertile and productive. Why hasn't this been enough?

Even after the warning of the Dust Bowl in the 1930s, enough topsoil to cover 500 thousand acres was blown or washed away in this country every year. This would make enough land to feed and clothe 175 thousand people for a year. In the near future, we are going to have to provide for millions more people than there are in this country today. We cannot afford to lose all that soil.

This is not our problem alone. It is a problem in many countries all over the world. The world's carpet of topsoil is wearing thin. And it is being used to feed increasing millions of people. It becomes more important all the time for the remaining topsoil to be kept where it belongs and used wisely. Other countries have been helped by the dramatic example of the damage done to the American earth in just three hundred years, and our efforts to stop that damage.

Our efforts to save our soil will have to continue and be increased. If they are not, our children's children may look out over miles of barren deserts, where now there are green fertile fields.

But we have a choice. The soil can be saved. The 1958 Yearbook of Agriculture, *Land*, puts the problem this way: "Now we are at a crossroads. At this moment in history, when our population is growing, the demands for many products of fields and forests mounts, and the face of the land is changing, we can choose, perhaps for the last time, what we are to do with our land, our country."

If every farmer and rancher, every worker on a farm or a ranch, felt strongly enough about his responsibility to the land and to the people who will use the land after him, the problem would certainly be solved. The choice would be made.

But there are not enough such people. Plans for soil and water conservation are made by technicians of the Soil Conservation Service. Individual farmers and ranchers, in nearly three thousand Soil Conservation Districts in our fifty states, Puerto Rico, and the Virgin Islands, cooperate in making these plans. But the plans are not always carried out. Some farmers and ranchers make a good start and then fall back into their old ways. Too often, they are interested in making more money from the land, as fast as they can, rather than in keeping the soil productive over a period of years. It isn't easy to plan for a future in which you yourself may not share.

It isn't even easy, sometimes, to see that taking care of the land will bring in a better income, in the long run, to the farmer or rancher who is living on the land right now.

Most of the land in this country is owned by individual people. The land is theirs. But that doesn't necessarily mean that they should be allowed to do whatever they want with it. The way land is used everywhere is everyone's business. Poor land frequently means poor people, not just on individual farms here and there, but often on the farm next door to the poor one, the farm down the road. Topsoil from dry uncovered earth on one farm can blow over onto the next one. Silt from a small mismanaged watershed can wash off the slopes and fill up reservoirs downstream. On hills where cattle or sheep have eaten off all the grass and trampled the earth, water in a heavy rain can rush down too fast and cause floods in the valley below. Farmers and cattlemen and foresters should not be allowed to think only of themselves. They are not living alone on their own island of earth. They are part of the whole world.

We value our freedom. It is not easy to decide to what extent the government should control what people do. But it is clear that the government may some day need to have some control over the use of the land, for the good of everyone.

Private landowners in the past have too often not been required to observe even the simplest rules of good land use. But this pattern is changing. It will have to change still more if we are to preserve our land.

In some states, Soil Conservation Districts, organized by local farmers, can regulate by law the use of the land. They may forbid harmful use of it and may require that a farmer adopt such measures as contour plowing, strip-cropping, and rotation of crops, in order to save his land.

In some states, too, a county government can itself take measures to control erosion. They hire someone to do the work on the land which the farmer should have done, and then he pays the bill.

Just as important as the care of crops and the land they grow on is the care of forests and woodlands. Trees were worth very little when our West was being settled. Loggers ripped the trees off hills and valleys and sent them downstream. Plenty of lumber was needed for houses. Lumberjacks were men of strength and courage leading dangerous lives in the woods. The story of Paul Bunyan and his blue ox is only a myth, but he was a symbol of the real strength and bigness of these men.

The cutting down of too many trees leaves the land uncovered. It can wash away. And the supply of trees is not endless. We could easily use up so much lumber that there would not be enough left in the future for such industries as building and paper-making.

Some forests, if they are managed well, renew themselves. New trees will grow there even if foresters do not plant them. In others, trees must be planted to replace those cut down, if the forest is to be maintained.

France has had since the seventeenth century a law that compels the planting of a tree for every one cut down.

In this country, some states have laws that provide that tree seedlings must be planted where necessary to replace all trees cut down. A lumberman in the state of Washington objected to this law. He said no one had a right to tell him what to do on his own land. Putting in seedlings would use up part of his profit, and he had a right to this profit as an American citizen. He took this to court in the state of Washington, and lost. Then he took it to a higher court, and another, until the case reached the Supreme Court of the United States in Washington, D.C. That court, too, ruled that this lumberman must obey his state law. The decision against him was called "A Pact with the Unborn." This was an important decision, stating that the government has the right to force lumbermen and farmers and cattlemen and all who care for the land to plan for those who will live on the land when they themselves are no longer there.

As American citizens we do have a right to make a fair profit, and sometimes this means a profit from the land or from whatever grows on the land. But we have responsibilities, too, toward other people who are living here now and will be living here in the future, toward our government, and toward the land itself.

All over this country young people, especially in rural areas, are learning about these responsibilities in their 4-H clubs and their local groups of Future Farmers of America. The Boy Scouts, too, the Girl Scouts, and the Camp Fire Girls are doing their share.

The 4-H stands for *head, heart, hands,* and *health.* Four-H members are boys and girls between the ages of ten and twenty-one who want to learn by doing in the fields of farming, homemaking, or community activities. The program of each club is based on the members' interests and needs. Farming is important to many of these boys and girls. Through the 4-H clubs they get a head start in learning to care for the land.

You may have belonged to a 4-H club or similar organization yourself. Or you may be a Future Farmer. The Future Farmers of America is an organization of farm boys who are studying agriculture as a career in their local high schools. Each Future Farmer carries out his own farming program, under the supervision of his agriculture teacher. With other Future Farmers he visits nearby agriculture experiment stations and Soil Conservation Districts to observe good farming and farm management.

The slogan of the Future Farmers is: "The successful farmer of tomorrow is the future farmer of today."

The Future Farmer who learns to take good care of the land from the very beginning will not be one who just does everything the way it has always been done, right or wrong. He will know how to keep his land from washing or blowing away. And he'll know how to maintain the fertility of his soil. This of course will be only part of his job. He will probably have to know how to raise healthy cattle or dairy cows, pigs or chickens. And to manage a modern farm he'll have to be somewhat of a scientist, and quite a businessman.

These Future Farmers are the best hope for the future of the land on the farms and ranches of America.

20: Machines on the Land

New machines for farming were invented in this country just as the Great Plains were being settled. Machines made it easier for the farmer to plow up more soil, plant more seed, and harvest more grain, on good land and on poor land.

The plows first used in this country were made entirely of wood. Wooden plows had been used in Europe for centuries. Then, in the early 1800s, a farmer in New Jersey invented a cast-iron plow. It was much more efficient than the wooden plow. At first, though, some suspicious farmers would have nothing to do with it. They insisted that the iron would poison the soil. They had to stop insisting when it became perfectly evident that the iron plow had no such effect on the soil at all.

In the 1830s the steel plow was developed. This cut the prairie sod much faster even than the cast-iron plow, and the earth didn't stick to it in lumps.

There was very little objection to the steel plow. It wasn't really new. It was just another kind of plow, and if iron didn't poison the soil, steel shouldn't either. Besides, anyone could see how fast that plow cut through the tough prairie sod. It seemed rather a miracle.

Blacksmiths all over the country started making steel plows. Improvements were developed. Factories were built. Steel plows were sold by thousands.

The plow was used to cut into the earth and turn it over. This left uneven clods all over the field. These clods were broken up and the soil made smooth by dragging a crude harrow over the field. The early harrow was a long board with a row of wooden prongs along the bottom of it. When the harrowing was finished, the farmer would scatter his seed by hand. Then he would pull a log across the field, so the soil would cover the seeds. Horses usually did the pulling, or oxen, but plowing and planting took long hours of hard work.

In time, the work became easier. It had to, if all those miles of prairie or plain were to be cultivated. It was not long before there were better harrows, with metal teeth or disks, for those who could afford to buy them. There were cultivators to loosen the soil beside the crops while they were growing. There were seed drills for putting the seed into the earth, much more efficiently than it could be done by hand.

One of the hardest jobs for the farmer was reaping, the cutting down of the ripe wheat or other crops. The earliest tool ever used for reaping was the sickle. It dates back at least to 3000 B.C. The scythe came a little later; it is a bigger sickle with a long handle. Some scythes have a cradle to catch the grain.

Machines for reaping were built in this country in the 1700s and the early 1800s. They might have been successful if someone had been able to manufacture a quantity of them and persuade the farmers to use them. But at first the farmers didn't think they needed these newfangled gadgets. They didn't see much wrong with the way they'd always done things. And the first reapers were not very efficient. They had a way of breaking down at just the wrong moment.

The first successful mechanical reaper was put together and presented to an audience of sceptical farmers by Cyrus McCormick in 1831. Cyrus McCormick's father had been trying out the idea of a reaper for years. He had studied the motions of his own arms and legs and back as he reaped with a scythe, and tried to reproduce them in wood and metal. This didn't work very well, but Cyrus took over where his father left off.

About the same time, a man named Obed Hussey patented his reaper, and for a while this one seemed likely to do better than Cyrus McCormick's. But Hussey was less of a businessman than McCormick. And he was satisfied with his reaper just the way it was. He didn't want to improve it. McCormick improved his over and over again.

Cyrus McCormick's first reaper could cut six acres a day, six times as fast as a man with a scythe could cut. Even so, many farmers weren't convinced. Most of them said they couldn't afford any such machine. McCormick made it easy for the farmers by letting them pay a little at a time, while they were using their reapers.

During the dozen or so years after he first demonstrated the reaper, Cyrus McCormick built and sold only a few of them. Obed Hussey was doing a little better. But then the idea began to catch on. This was partly because McCormick refused to give up. He thought he had a workable idea, and he kept on improving his machine and trying to sell it. And his success came partly because in the long run farmers knew a good thing when they saw it. At least, when they saw it work, and found out it might even save them money in the end.

By 1847 the McCormick factory in Chicago was selling four thousand reapers a year. In 1863, just sixteen years later, forty thousand were sold. Cyrus McCormick built more and more factories for making reapers and other machines.

With the reaping machine, miles and miles of wheat could be reaped on the plains with the labor of only a few men, in record time. This is what this country needed in order to grow and prosper. During the Civil War, when thousands of men were fighting instead of working on the land, this country grew more wheat than before, rather than less. It was not a miracle that accomplished this. It was the reaper. People became a little drunk with this success, this plenty. The land, it seemed, would go on yielding these full harvests forever.

Threshing, separating the grain from the straw, was another job that took plenty of time and hard work. The first successful threshing machine was made not long after McCormick's first reaper. Soon after that, combines were invented, machines that could do both reaping and threshing. Huge combines are used now for gathering the miles and miles of wheat on the Great Plains. Smaller one-man combines are used on smaller farms. There are more than a million of these in use today.

There are, besides, special machines for such jobs are cutting and binding hay, picking cotton or corn, digging peanuts, and so on. A grain drill can plant sixteen or more rows of seed at once and drop fertilizer in at the same time. Even the plow has become mechanized. A modern gang plow, for instance, turns over the soil as if it were four plows in a row, and it is pulled by a tractor.

Farming more land with better machines meant more food for the growing population. And it meant more leisure for farmers. In 1830 it took a man fifty-eight hours to produce an acre of wheat. Now, on our Great Plains, it takes less than two hours.

This progress was all to the good—or, so it seemed. But in the long run, some of the results of using efficient machines were not good for the soil. Heavy machines running over the land pack the soil down tight. Water soaks into such tight-packed soil too slowly.

With these big machines, too, it became possible for the farmer, without more effort, to farm more land and grow more crops, while the soil itself was being worn out. It was easier to be careless with bigger and bigger pieces of land. It got so it was hard to see that anything was wrong with the land, because a farmer could get at least some profit out of it, even if his land was already losing its fertility—if he had a big enough piece of land. And if he hadn't bought more machines than he could afford.

The time might come, though, when that land might not be good enough to bring him any profit at all. Or the good fertile top of it might blow or wash away.

More than two-thirds of the people in the world work at farming or other jobs related to agriculture. But very few countries have even a few of the machines that the farmers of the United States use in their work. In most countries, farming methods have hardly changed at all for hundreds of years. Farmers use simple wooden plows; they scatter their seed by hand. Often they drop poor seed in exhausted earth and suffer from hunger because the crop is poor.

The Food and Agriculture Organization of the United Nations has been helping many of these farmers, all over the world. Complicated machines are often not a solution to their problems, especially in places where there are plenty of people to do the work. Often what is needed is better plows, with horses to pull them; hand-operated seed drills, which do not waste seed; scythes with cradles for catching grain, instead of short-handled sickles. Changes like this are easily accepted by the people, and they often mean the difference between near-starvation and having enough to eat.

Perhaps something has been lost in the use of big machines, after all. It is not so easy, now, for the farmer to feel close to his land.

There can be joy in plowing and harrowing your own earth as you walk over it on your own feet. Joy in planting, too, the joy of the farmer feeling the slippery seeds in his hand as he scatters them over the earth, knowing that they will sprout and grow into grain.

In *Giants in the Earth*, Rölvaag says of Per Hansa, who had cut down his wheat himself and was ready to bind it:

"Per Hansa was in a rare mood that afternoon. Now he was binding his own wheat, his hands oily with the sap of the new-cut stems; a fine oil it was, too. . . . His body seemed to grow a little with every bundle he tied; he walked as if on springs; a strength the like of which he had never felt before ran through his muscles. How good it was to be alive! . . . He tied the ripe, heavy bundles, gave them a twist, and there stood the shock! As he looked at them he laughed to himself joyously. . . ."

This kind of joy comes most easily to the farmer of small fertile fields. With his own hands, and the hands of those who work with him, this farmer can plow and plant and reap only the few acres that can be finished in the time from dawn to sunset, in this old slow way. In this country, he would probably be glad to trade this joy for a bigger farm, with efficient machines. He would have a better chance, then, of making a good living.

There cannot be much joy, anywhere in the world, for the farmer who throws his seed onto tired eroded earth, knowing the crop will be a poor one.

In this country, we need machines on the land, to help grow food for our many people. And we need machines, too, to help feed the rest of the world.

Even more important than machines, everywhere, is the care of the soil itself, whether it is tilled by machines that roar over it or by man himself with simple hand tools.

21: Care of the Soil

Before the soil itself can be taken care of, it has to be kept from washing away and blowing away. Erosion does more damage to the land than any one other thing.

We have already talked about ways of preventing erosion. Let's sum this up, and go on from there.

First, contour farming. On gentle slopes, just plowing and planting horizontally, along the sides of the slope, following its curves, will help prevent water erosion.

On steeper slopes, contour strip-cropping may be needed. That is, strips of close-growing, erosion-resistant crops, such as grass, clover, or wheat are alternated with strips of clean-tilled row crops, such as corn.

Slopes that are still steeper, but not too steep for cultivation, can be terraced on the contour. Terraces may be any one of three types—bench, graded, or level. Terraces cross the slopes in earthen platforms like steps. Bench terracing is the kind that was developed in early times. It is almost as old as agriculture itself. Modified bench-type terraces are used extensively in the citrus groves of California and in Puerto Rico.

The graded terrace is a structure with a broad base which helps the water to run off steep slopes without causing erosion. Level terraces are designed to hold the little rain that falls in dry regions, so that crops can be grown there.

Stubble-mulch tillage helps prevent both wind and water erosion by providing a cover for the protection of cultivated fields. The cultivators, machines that are used in preparing the fields for planting, leave stubble and straw and other remains of crops on or near the surface of the soil. This mulch protects the soil from the sharp splash of raindrops in a heavy rain. The soil is kept porous so that water will soak in. Stubble mulch also makes tiny dams all over the field, to slow down the runoff water. Soil treated this way is not likely to blow away, either.

Sometimes, instead of stubble mulching, cover crops are planted for winter protection. Cover crops may be wheat or rye or forage grasses. Their roots help hold down the soil and hold the rainfall until the soil absorbs it.

Besides grasses and grains, there are other plants which grow close together and hold the soil with their roots. Kudzu is a vine which at one time was used extensively in the South for holding soil on the sides of gullies. Clovers, grasses, and other plants are now taking its place. Deep-rooted trees and shrubs hold the soil.

Little dams called check dams are used to control the flow of water in gullies or on terraces. All these things help slow up runoff water and reduce erosion. Water gets a better chance to sink into the soil.

Of course, one of the best ways of preventing erosion on any piece of land is by not giving it the wrong kind of use in the first place. Many steep slopes, for instance, should not be used for growing crops at all, even with terraces.

In the Dust Bowl of the early Thirties, when Franklin D. Roosevelt was President, shelterbelts were extensively planted in the Great Plains. These were strips or belts of trees and shrubs planted along the sides of fields and farms, where they would act as buffers against the wind. The Forest Service worked on this from 1934 to 1942. Seedling trees which had been started in a nursery were usually planted, because they had a fairly good chance to survive. Little trees grown from seed would have had too hard a time on the windy plains.

Many people thought the whole idea was silly. Trees were never meant to grow on the plains, they said. They thought the President wanted to plant a forest right down the middle of the plains.

But it wasn't a forest he wanted. It was just strips of trees. And the trees did grow. When the Forest Service checked up on its shelterbelts in 1954, three-quarters of the trees had survived, in spite of considerable neglect and browsing by cattle.

The planting of trees as field windbreaks, or shelterbelts, was taken over by the Soil Conservation Service in 1942, as part of its soil and water conservation program.

Shelterbelts help save soil by breaking the force of the wind. Snow piles up against them in winter and then melts into water in the spring. Birds thrive in the branches of the trees. Farmers were surprised that the idea worked. Now they like these windbreaks so well that millions of trees are planted by farmers each year, in cooperation with the Soil Conservation Service, Soil Conservation Districts, and other organizations.

There is, as we have seen, nothing more important in the care of the land than stopping erosion. Soil that is washed away is of no use to anyone, unless it happens to be deposited on broad flat valleys beside flooding rivers. This happened in ancient Egypt. It still happens to some extent along other rivers. But it is the exception rather than the rule. And what is deposited may be sand, gravel, and worthless debris.

Once erosion is stopped, there are other problems. Soil may stay where it belongs and still be useless. Not all the soil on the earth is naturally fertile. And of course, much of what used to be fertile soil has been worn out, often by having the same crop grown on it year after year.

Since ancient times, man has been searching for ways of preserving and even improving the fertility of the soil. We have seen how the Romans rotated crops in order to preserve the soil. So did the medieval peasants. Toward the end of the Middle Ages, some farmers had learned that planting clover and certain other crops on a field and then plowing them under made the soil more productive. Farmers learned to give back to the land the manure of their cattle.

During the nineteenth century, the science of chemistry was applied for the first time to the soil. Baron Justus von Liebig and other chemists discovered that plants feed on mineral salts dissolved in water. Just how the plants did this was not known, and only the principal minerals were discovered. But this discovery made possible the manufacture of fertilizers that supplied these three principal minerals to the plants: nitrogen, potash, and phosphorus.

This was a great discovery. At first, as often happens, most farmers would have none of it. They had been farming for years, and their fathers for many years before them. How could a chemist who worked in a laboratory tell them anything about growing crops?

The objections of the farmers were understandable. But Liebig *could* tell them something about growing crops, and he did tell them. Once the idea was accepted, many experts went to the other extreme from the farmers. They decided that this knowledge of chemicals was all anyone needed to grow plants in the soil. Wheat could grow tall and bear grain in soil treated only with chemicals. Plants could even grow in a solution of these chemicals in water.

But this was not the whole story, after all. The workings of nature are not that simple, and man cannot duplicate them so easily, if at all. Soil that is given no treatment other than chemical fertilizers often becomes dry and hard. The organic part of the soil, the part that is teeming with bacteria, moulds and other fungi, and such, in the midst of naturally growing and decaying matter, ceases to exist. Earthworms cannot live in such soil. Plants do not grow well. In time, there is not even enough life in the soil to respond to the chemical fertilizers themselves.

Plants grown only with chemical fertilizers may, for a time, look as big and green as those grown in organic soil. But they are not the same. The other mineral and so-called trace elements that are missing in the soil and the fertilizer will be missing in the plants, too. The chemically raised plants have been found to contain much less protein than organically grown plants. Protein is a very important part of our food. Insects for some reason prefer the inferior chemically grown plants; so much so that it seems almost impossible to get rid of them on such plants.

To people, on the other hand, vegetables and grain grown on good organic soil taste better. People and animals that eat these crops are stronger and healthier than those that eat crops grown mainly on chemicals.

What should we do, then? Throw out the chemicals entirely? Some farmers have done this. They have grown lush and disease-free crops, on land that had at least a trace of fertility, by using animal manures, green manures, and other organic materials. Compost heaps, especially in small gardens, can be used to make humus for the soil. Humus is the part of the soil which is formed from decaying plant and animal wastes. Bacteria and fungi keep the decay going.

A compost heap consists of layers of soil, vegetable matter such as weeds, and sometimes animal wastes, which decay to make humus. The humus is then mixed with the soil of the garden. Earthworms tunnel through the soil in such a garden, letting in air and improving its structure.

When the composting is done on the land itself, where the crops are growing, it is called sheet composting.

But we should not, after all, throw out the chemical fertilizers entirely. The soil may be lacking in minerals which cannot be supplied by compost. Fertilizer will supply them. Besides, though we cannot really change the processes of nature, we can make them happen faster. Gardening by entirely organic methods may simply be too slow for many farmers. They have to make enough money to live on, not five years hence, but right now. Chemical fertilizer can help. It can also make it possible for the farmer to produce rapidly quantities of green manure which he can mix with his soil. Fertilizer even helps cattle to produce more manure for the soil, because the fertilized fields will provide plenty of grass for the cattle to eat.

As we have seen, not all the natural soils in the world have the right balance of minerals. The soil on the Great Plains does have such a balance. Much soil in Florida, however, such as the drained soil in the Everglades, is lacking in important minerals. There are plenty of plants growing there, but they are all of poor quality.

On the other side of the world, in Pakistan, millions of acres of land are now unusable for growing crops because there is too much salt in the soil, too much of the wrong minerals, deposited there for many years by irrigation water.

This is so important for Pakistan that our government has promised aid to the people in getting the salt out of their soil. Chemical fertilizers cannot do this job. Neither can humus.

Too much chemical fertilizer will damage the soil even if it is rich in organic material. The modern farmer who wants to use up-to-date fertilizers and tools must be a scientist and a mechanic as well as a man versed in the ways of nature. There is little room for guesswork.

No one knows how much the soil in this country has been damaged by too little attention to the organic qualities of the soil, but the damage has been great. Soil without organic matter becomes hard and dry. Water cannot sink into it. Sheet erosion may wear it away.

Our overuse of chemicals may at least have served as a warning to other countries. Western European farmers, for instance, while they have used fertilizers, never went overboard in their use. They have kept close to the good organic way of farming which they inherited from their fathers. This way of farming has kept the soil fertile from one generation to the next. Change is not always for the better. The way the land has been used by Western European farmers for hundreds of years needs very little change.

"The best fertilizer on any farm is the footsteps of the owner." This was a saying of Confucius in China more than a thousand years ago. It is still true today. There is nothing better for a farm than an owner, or it may be a tenant or any worker, who knows the earth because he has walked over it, acre by acre, and studied the soil beneath his feet.

The good farmer looks back as his plow turns a furrow to see if the soil crumbles as good soil should. He knows as he looks at the earth whether it is rich and fertile, whether it has enough humus. As his crops grow, he watches them, and his practiced eye can tell whether they are healthy or not. He learns what his soil is like, and what it can do, by farming it. He will use modern machinery, and fertilizer where it is needed, but these will not take the place of his knowledge of the soil itself.

Louis Bromfield was a writer and farmer who spent many years in France, where he learned the ways of French farmers with their soil. When World War II came, he returned to the valley where he had been born, in southern Ohio. There he bought several run-down farms and proceeded to show how hard and apparently useless soil can be made fertile again, without spending much more than the average farmer can afford. He wanted to prove that misused land can become an asset to the farmer and to the country. It can even become good business.

Much of Mr. Bromfield's topsoil was gone, washed away through years of erosion. What was left was mostly a subsoil made up of many kinds of crumbled rock that had been stirred together by the great glacier, long ago. With the right kind of care, this could become good soil within a few years.

Many farmers have not been so fortunate. Beneath the washed-off topsoil on many farms is solid rock or hardpan or blue clay. No amount of manure or fertilizer will make topsoil out of that.

Mr. Bromfield used contour plowing or strip cropping or terracing on slopes, much as we have described them. The soil itself was restored by adding organic material in the form of green-manure crops and animal manures. This was mixed loosely with the soil where the crops were growing, and there, through the natural action of bacteria, it decayed and formed humus. This, as we have seen, is called sheet composting.

Commercial fertilizers were used where needed, but no more than most farmers would use. Lime helped, too. It kept the soil from being too acid for the plants and did other good things for it. Not all soils need lime, however.

On his renewed fields Mr. Bromfield grew much more corn, and more of other crops, than the average amounts grown all over this country.

Green manuring was an important part of Mr. Bromfield's restoration of his land. Not all plants can be used for this. Those most often used belong to the plant family called legumes. All legumes enrich the soil where they grow. Bacteria in small lumps on their roots change the nitrogen from the air into a kind of nitrogen that plants can use. Clover and lespedeza (a bush clover) are legumes. So are beans, peas, chick-peas, and alfalfa. When any of these plants are mixed with the soil at the end of a growing season, their roots give nitrogen to the soil for the next season's crops. Nitrogen is essential for the growth of plants.

The clovers and lespedeza also hold the soil tight and so are good for controlling erosion.

We have seen that Edmund Ruffin, in the South before the Civil War, used various kinds of peas as green manure. More people should have listened to him.

It was the plow that broke the plains. It was the plow that ripped up the rough earth which had been cleared of forests in the East. Long before that time, the plow had helped in the development of early civilizations. But as it became more efficient, there were some farmers who were not sure the work of the plow was always good for the earth.

There was Edward Faulkner. He wrote a book called *Plowman's Folly,* in which he explained why he thought the moldboard plow, which was so efficient at turning over the earth, should not be used at all. He had found, he said, that this plow turned over and buried all the plants and other matter from the surface of the earth and left the soil uncovered, exposed to sun and rain and wind. The plow also packed this surface trash into a tight narrow layer which could not become healthy soil.

Louis Bromfield tried out Mr. Faulkner's ideas. In general, he agreed with Faulkner. At least, he was against so-called *good* plowing, which buried the surface trash too tight and too deep. On land that has become hard and dry, or where the sod is heavy and tough, a plow must be used. But it is best to plow roughly, leaving organic material near the surface, where it will decay and absorb water.

Instead of the plow, or after plowing, a farmer may use a disk harrow, rows of sharp disks which cut up the lumps of earth without digging deep.

There are other methods to use on different kinds of soil. The modern farmer has to know his business. He has to be ready to change, too. More and more is being learned about the care of the soil. Experts develop new and better machines. And here and there in the world are those persistent men who have watched the earth and the plants that grow and decay in it and have decided to experiment with wholly natural ways of growing crops.

One of these men was Sir Albert Howard, who was knighted by the British Crown for his contribution to agriculture. When Sir Albert was an agricultural aide in India at the beginning of this century, he observed that the natives there grew crops without chemical fertilizers or poison sprays. They did not seem to need them. Sir Albert decided that the key to a fertile soil was humus. He made compost from all sorts of manure and refuse and spread this compost on his fields. The humus that resulted was full of bacteria and fungi. Some of the antibiotics which are used to combat disease today grow in such soil. Trace minerals were present, small quantities of minerals other than those found in commercial fertilizer. The bacteria and fungi helped all the minerals to dissolve, so they could be used by the plants. The soil itself was alive, and the plants that grew in it were rich in the vitamins, minerals, and proteins which bring health to people and animals. Oxen which were fed crops grown on Sir Albert Howard's organic soil were free of diseases which plagued other animals in India.

Humus made as Sir Albert Howard made it is perhaps the best fertilizer. Why, then, is this process not used everywhere? Not all farmers believe in it. Not all know how to do it. And many cannot afford to use this method entirely. Sir Albert's process required a great deal of labor, and this was cheap in India. It would be too expensive here.

Mr. Bromfield's compromise seems to be the best solution for this country. The processes which he used in restoring organic material to his land and rebuilding his topsoil were nature's own processes. They were speeded up several thousand times by the use of man-made compost, green-manure crops and animal manures, and a certain amount of commercial fertilizer.

The greatest need of United States soils is for more organic materials. Nature makes organic matter in topsoil slowly, over thousands of years, leaf by leaf, as one delicate blade of grass after another grows and dies in the earth. We would be in a sad fix indeed if we had to wait for nature to supply these organic materials to the soil.

As it is, farmers are growing more and better wheat all the time, more and better corn. Some of it perhaps only *looks* better. You can't tell by just looking whether plants grown on soil fertilized mostly with artificial chemicals contain all the life-giving minerals and vitamins and proteins they should have. They may just be bulky with carbohydrates.

Before chemical fertilizers and efficient machines were used, land that was wearing out would give warning. The corn grown on it would be shorter, the ears smaller. Wheat would be thin and stunted. It would be time to move on or, better, to improve the soil.

But land that has been stimulated with artificial fertilizers gives no warning. It may keep on producing bumper crops, year after year. Not necessarily good grain, but plenty of it. And then it fails. Even with fertilizer, the soil will not produce as it used to. It is worn out.

Farmers who have used conservation methods know that they pay better in the long run than methods which wear out the soil. But many farmers have still to learn.

We grow so much wheat and other crops that surpluses pile up. It should go to people who are starving in other parts of the world. Some of it does. Through its Food for Peace plan, the United States has provided school lunches to millions of children in underdeveloped countries who otherwise might not have any lunch at all. Food has sometimes been used instead of money in helping many of the people of these countries.

It is not easy to transport all this wheat and other food across the oceans. There are still huge bins of it here. Surely this is prosperity from the land. It makes us all feel good to hear about it.

But there are things we have forgotten. Two years of drought on the Plains, such as we had at the time of our Dust Bowl, could wipe out those surpluses. Drought on the northern Great Plains threatened to wipe out any possible surplus of grain in that area in the summer of 1961. Parts of six states were declared drought disaster areas, eligible for aid from the United States government.

In the years to come, our increasing population will use up a large part of our surpluses. We have 185 million people in this country now, and three million more each year. What we can produce right now, instead of giving us surpluses, may not even be enough in the future.

We must take better care of our land. We must stop trying to subdue nature, trying to make nature do what we decide she should do. Instead, we will have to work with nature, to save the soil on our fields and plains and hillsides. We must do this for ourselves and for all the people who will come after us.

22: Water on the Land

Land without water is a desert. Land with too much water is a swamp or a marsh. Both these kinds of land provide homes for a variety of wildlife, but neither is good land for growing food for people. The way land is used often depends on how much water falls on the earth as rain, or how much water can be brought to the land from below the surface, from streams, or from reservoirs. Sometimes, too, the use of land may depend on how much water can be taken away from it.

The places in the world which have just enough water, at just the right times, are few. The places that have this and fertile earth besides, and are not too hot or too cold, are even fewer. Of all the millions of people in the world, only a small fraction can live in such places.

The rest of the people in the world live on land that is not quite so good or not good at all. Often, they do not have enough water for growing crops when they need it and where they need it. For many hundreds of years man has been using his ingenuity to bring water to his fields in dry seasons. He has even brought water to the dry deserts of the world.

We have seen how irrigation changed the way of life of early man. No one knows how long ago irrigation itself developed. It required considerable skill, even at first. But irrigation as a science has developed only in modern times. Modern irrigation is carried on with dams and pumps and other devices which early man could not even have dreamed of.

In North America, in parts of what is now southern New Mexico and Arizona, man irrigated his fields thousands of years ago, long before any history was written. Archaeologists have found the remains of canals and reservoirs that were built that far back.

Many years later, perhaps only a thousand years ago, Pueblo Indians dug irrigation ditches through the valleys below their high cliff dwellings. They caught rain water in their ditches and stored it behind small dams.

Not far from these Pueblos, in the valleys of the Gila and Salt rivers in what is now Arizona, the Hohokam Indians dug miles of irrigation ditches. This was about A.D. 600 to 700. For hundreds of years the Hohokams kept on digging these ditches and keeping them in good condition, so water from the rivers could flow through their fields. Some of the ditches were as much as twenty-five feet wide, almost as wide as a modern city street. Some were fifteen feet deep. A tall man could stand on the head of another tall man in one of these deep ditches and still not look out over the top of it. Some single ditches were as long as fifteen to sixteen miles. A network of ditches could add up to 150 miles.

All these ditches were made by the Hohokams with no animals to help them and no metal tools. Imagine digging such deep ditches in dry earth entirely by hand, without even a metal shovel. What tools did these people use? Sharp stones, perhaps, with wooden handles. Nothing better.

These remarkable people flourished in the towns they built in the desert. Living was not too hard. There was time for dancing, for the making of pottery and the weaving of beautiful baskets.

But about A.D. 1400, the Hohokams disappeared. Their name means, in the Pima language, those who have vanished. No one is sure why the Hohokams disappeared or where they went. Perhaps there was no longer enough water in the rivers. Perhaps there was finally too much salt in the earth from the irrigation water. Water was always evaporating in the hot sun and leaving on the fields the salts it had picked up from the earth as it flowed through the canals.

Later, Spanish settlers came to this same part of North America, our Southwest. The Spaniards understood very well how to irrigate this land. It was not unlike the semidesert and mountain country which had been irrigated in their own country for many years, but there was much more of it—miles and miles. These Spaniards settled along the rivers. Mexicans did, too.

Mormons came from the eastern part of the United States, seeking freedom to practice their own religion. They set up a very efficient irrigation system on land that was dry, for a large part of the year, in Utah.

In the early days of this country, however, irrigation of the land was the exception, rather than the rule. There seemed to be plenty of well-watered land without bothering with places of little rain. The few men who saw the possibilities in irrigating much of the dry land in this country were laughed at or ignored.

Only a few thousand acres of land—and this is not much in a country as big as ours—were irrigated before the late 1800s. In 1902, however, the federal government decided that something should be done about the dry lands, after all. In that year the Reclamation Service was created, under the United States Department of the Interior. In 1924 its name was changed to Bureau of Reclamation. Its purpose was to reclaim land, and this meant, first of all, bringing water to dry places. Irrigating vast miles of desert and semidesert is too big a job for any individual, too big even for any state government to undertake. The federal government had to do the job.

Water of rivers was to be stored behind huge dams and carried to the fields in seemingly endless canals. The dry brown places in this country would be made green with growing things.

The first great dam, finished by the Reclamation Service in 1910, was Roosevelt Dam, built on the Salt River in Arizona, to store water for the lands once irrigated by the Hohokam Indians.

Another is Hoover Dam, or Boulder Dam, on the Colorado River, finished in 1936. Many miles of farmland are irrigated by water from Lake Mead, the reservoir behind Hoover Dam. The water of the reservoir also turns turbines that provide power for huge electric generators.

Grand Coulee Dam, on the Columbia River in the state of Washington, is the largest concrete dam in this country. Its reservoir, Franklin D. Roosevelt Lake, will in time irrigate more than a million acres of land. There are other dams along the Columbia River, all part of the Columbia Basin Project.

Grand Coulee Dam was built in the 1930s, the years of the Dust Bowl and the wanderings of the Dust Bowl refugees. Some of these refugees got jobs working on the dam. The Bureau of Reclamation sent the folk singer Woody Guthrie to talk with the workers and listen to what they said and sang about their work. Out of this grew twenty-six songs which were recorded by the Bonneville Power Administration.

The whole Columbia Basin Project was something to stir anyone's imagination: In the midst of the years of the Dust Bowl, to think of green plants springing up on all the dry land that was going to be watered by the river.

The Bureau of Reclamation has not had just one long story of success, however. Sometimes the planners have considered only one part of a river, the part where they wanted to build a dam. They would have done well to consider the river all the way upstream, above the dam, and the land on both sides of the river. The watershed of the river, the uplands where it starts, may be neglected, the land perhaps laid bare by the cutting down of too many trees, or by letting too many cattle graze there. Topsoil from this watershed washes into the river, and down the river into reservoirs. In the reservoirs this silt can't wash down any more. It sinks to the bottom and starts filling up the reservoir.

Lake Mead, at Hoover Dam, is continually filling up with silt which is brought down by the Colorado River. The silt carried into this reservoir each year has averaged enough to cover about a hundred thousand acres with soil one foot deep. Too many cattle and sheep have overgrazed the watershed lands above the reservoir. Too many trees have been cut off the mountainsides.

This has happened to other reservoirs, behind other dams, such as the Elephant Butte Reservoir on the Rio Grande River in New Mexico. It even happens to rivers, where they do not move fast enough to carry along the silt. The Rio Grande River itself has been filling up.

Some of the land irrigated by the Elephant Butte Reservoir is where the Spanish settlers dug their irrigation ditches in the late sixteenth and early seventeenth centuries. This reservoir could irrigate many more acres of land today if silt were not filling up the river and clogging the irrigation canals.

As we have seen, this is an ancient problem. The Babylonians did not solve it. We have not solved it entirely, either. But we are learning how to.

One way to prevent the silting up of reservoirs and rivers is to study all of a river and the land on both sides of it, including its watershed and all the streams that run into the river itself. Silt in rivers comes from topsoil washed off land upstream. Any plan for a river or a reservoir is likely to run into trouble unless the plan includes keeping the topsoil where it belongs on all the slopes of the watershed.

This kind of planning is a big job. Perhaps it cannot be done completely. But the Tennessee Valley Authority has very nearly accomplished this by making plans for the whole of the Tennessee River and its valley, and carrying out those plans. Dams on the river control the floods that used to pour over the land. They provide power, too, for the generating of electricity that is used in homes and in factories. Farmers along the river have been taught how to keep their soil from washing away, and how to grow good crops. Too much grazing of cattle was not a problem here, because this is not cattle-raising country.

There is still much work to be done in the Tennessee Valley. But the plan for the valley and its rivers and its watershed has shown what can be done. People from all over the world have come to see the TVA and take ideas back to their own countries.

Some parts of this country where there is not much rain are farmed without irrigation. This kind of farming is called dry farming or dry-land farming. Of course, the land is not completely dry. If it were, nothing could grow there. Dry farming can be done on land that gets fourteen to eighteen inches of rain or snow or both in a year, which is not much moisture. It means careful planning and good conservation methods all the time: contour plowing, strip-cropping, keeping the earth spongy and soft so it can absorb the little rain that falls. Usually, in dry farming, the land is left without a crop, without even weeds that might use up too much of the moisture, every other summer. This is summer fallowing.

Grains can be grown by dry farming; they do not need large amounts of water. All over the world, land with just this small amount of rainfall is farmed. People *have* to use this kind of land. Otherwise they could not possibly grow enough food. But all this land would grow better crops, and a greater variety of them, if more water could be brought to it. Irrigation is even used in some places, such as the eastern part of the United States, where there is usually enough rain but better crops can be grown if farmers do not depend entirely on the rain.

There are many kinds of conservation. They are all related to one another. Soil conservation is only one kind; it would not mean much without conservation of water. Conservation of our forests, too, is related to the soil, because forests grow on the land. Important, too, is conservation of the wildlife in the forests, the fish that swim in the waters of the sea and in the rivers, and the birds that fly overhead and have their nests on the earth or near it. Any one of these kinds of conservation could fill a book. And yet, conservation is quite a new idea in the world. The few people who had something to say about it in the distant past were like voices crying in the wilderness. To most people, conservation did not seem important. Resources seemed endless.

But in the early 1900s in this country, conservation became a very live subject. Under the leadership of Gifford Pinchot, the Forest Service in this country began really planning for the use and care of forests in such a way that we would not just be wiping them out. As we have seen, soil conservation got a start under Hugh Hammond Bennett. President Theodore Roosevelt was especially interested in conservation and did much to promote it. So did President Franklin D. Roosevelt in the 1930s.

The 1930s saw not only the Dust Bowl, but the greatest depression this country had ever known. Many people were out of work in those years. Of these, many were young people, and more than three million of them were organized by the Federal Government as the Civilian Conservation Corps. The CCC was conservation on the march. Under expert leadership, young men invaded the mountains, the forests, the swamps, the deserts and the grasslands, and did whatever needed to be done. Wells and springs were improved, dams were built to hold water, trails and roads were constructed. The boys repaired irrigation ditches, plowed on the contour around slopes, made terraces on hills, planted trees, kept topsoil from blowing and washing away. Some built cabins in the woods for hikers, or put up fire towers and ranger stations.

Many of the CCC boys had never been out of the city before. Some had never been away from home. But something good happened to them when they dug a shovel into the earth or went to work in the woods with an ax. They were sending money home, where it was needed. But they were doing even more for themselves. While they grew strong and healthy in the outdoors, close to the earth, they were learning what it meant to work with others at a job that was worth doing, a job that was important for their country—restoring and saving our natural resources.

We have taken a long look at the use and misuse of the land in our country, partly because this land is closest to us, and partly because this has been a country well known for its destruction of the land and its heroic efforts, in the recent past, to make up for that destruction. Now let's see what has been happening to the land in some other parts of the world.

23: Land Use in Africa and South America

Africa has tremendous problems in the use of its land. Land has been laid bare by the cutting down of forests, by the grazing of too many cattle, sheep, and goats. Soil has been exhausted by too much growing of the same crops, over and over again, on the same piece of earth. Erosion results.

So far this might be a description of what has happened on our own continent. But there are important ways in which the continent of Africa differs from North America. Except for a fringe of fertile land bordering on seas and oceans, the northern part of Africa consists mainly of the largest and least fertile desert in the world, the Sahara. There are other deserts in Africa, too. Deserts are such a special problem in the world that this book has a separate chapter about them.

Even more important for a study of the land is difference in climate. North America is in the temperate zone, with cold or cool winters and warm summers. Europe is in the temperate zone, too. But all of Africa except the most northern and southern parts is in the tropical zone. The central part of the continent is covered with damp tropical forest.

North and south of this are broad areas called savannas, covered with stiff grass and clumps of trees. Rain is infrequent on the hot savannas. North and south of the savannas, and in East Africa, are the areas called the bush. There you will find thorny bushes, little trees, and short grass. Of course, these areas are not sharply defined.

Hot sun pours down on tropical Africa almost all the time. Only in the mountains and on the high plateaus in the eastern part of Africa is it sometimes cool. There is not much rain over most of the hot land, except in the tropical forest. Along the equator this forest is drenched in rain, and it is called the rain forest.

This damp forest is the jungle, thick and lush with a tangled growth of trees and bushes and vines. The jungle looks as if it grew from the most fertile soil in the world. But this is not what happens in the tropics.

In the temperate zone, most of the fertility is in the soil, at least until it is used up. But in the tropics, plants and animals grow and decay in the heat so fast that most of the fertility is busily at work in the plants and animals that are living on the soil. Plants and animals grow quickly, die, and return organic matter to the earth. This organic matter almost at once becomes part of new plants and animals. There is no winter period of rest.

In its natural state, tropical land can go on this way indefinitely. It spends its fertility with reckless speed, but the fertility is replaced by fresh organic matter just as fast. The soil maintains its own balance.

People have lived on the tropical land in Africa for thousands of years. At first, they disturbed the balance of nature not at all. Later, and until rather recent times, they disturbed this balance only a little. The people who cultivated the earth used the same methods early farmers used in other parts of the world. That is, they would clear a small plot of land, plant it with a food crop over and over again, until the soil was worn out, and then move on. Since the soil itself held little fertility in these tropical regions, three or four crops might be all these primitive farmers could grow on one piece of land before it was worn out. If the land they had used was not too exhausted, it would return to forest or jungle, and the rapid cycle of fertility, from the earth to lush growth and back to the earth, would begin again. The same land would not be used again by people for many years.

Usually these primitive farmers cleared their land by burning, where the growth was not too wet. It would have been very difficult to do it any other way. Burning reduced the fertility of the soil somewhat, but land that was burned so infrequently could recover.

Herders of cattle burned off wide areas of grasses and shrubs, and forests of trees, so they would have new fodder for their animals. This did more damage to the land than the burning off of land just here and there by the farmers. Land that has been forest tends to become forest again. To keep the land clear for cattle, it must be burned over and over. Each time, the soil becomes poorer. We have seen how the burning off of hillsides in Ethiopia provided rich silt for the Nile Valley in Egypt, as the soil washed off the hillsides in the heavy rains and went down the river.

When Europeans came to Africa, they saw the lush tropical vegetation. Such richness, they thought, must come from tremendously fertile soil. Surely all that was needed was to introduce scientific methods and grow bumper crops on thousands of acres.

It did not work out that way. European methods of farming were not suited to tropical soils at all. The fertility was not in the soil. An untidy mixture of different crops, each adding something to the organic process, is better for tropical soils than the European idea of neat rows of single crops.

Tropical land that was tilled by Europeans was worn out almost before anyone knew what had happened.

The Europeans helped the Africans to overcome diseases, prevent starvation, and live at peace with neighboring tribes. No one could reasonably object to that. The Africans, however, often did object to the Europeans being there at all.

The result of the help brought by the Europeans was more and more people on the land, living in ways that were suited to fewer people. In addition to this, they began growing crops not just to feed themselves but to sell to other people. Tobacco and cotton became cash crops. Plots of land closer and closer together were cleared. Land had to be used again much too soon after it had been left fallow. Soil that would need forty or fifty years to build up its full fertility after growing crops would be planted again after only a few years. It was soon worn out.

The story was even worse with the cattle. The Europeans overcame the diseases that had killed many of the cattle. Again, this was a humane thing to do. But for years the diseases had kept the cattle from becoming too numerous. To many African tribes cattle are wealth. The most important thing in their lives is to have more cattle. Now, the land cannot feed them all. Overgrazing has stripped all the vegetation off much of the land in Africa. Soil washes down the hills and off the overgrazed fields. Ditches grow into gullies. Rain cannot sink into the hard-baked earth. The underground supply of water grows less and less. Wells go dry.

African land needs more water, not less. In too many places, there was never quite enough, and in the deserts, almost none at all. Now the deserts are becoming larger.

The destruction of forests in Africa may have affected the rainfall. Trees take in water through their roots, along with food for their growth, and they give off moisture into the air, by transpiration. A heavy concentration of this moisture in the sky helps make clouds, and clouds bring rain. Without the trees, there is more heat, and less rain.

The Union of South Africa, in the southern part of the continent, has a climate much more congenial to Europeans than the tropical regions. Thousands of Europeans went there to live in the nineteenth and early twentieth centuries. The veldt (South African for savanna) was ideal for grazing. In many places it has been burned every year, by both Africans and Europeans, so it can produce a quick new crop of grass. Too many cattle graze on this quick crop, which is poorer every year, as the soil grows poorer. Farms have been thoughtlessly set up on steep hillsides. Gully erosion and sheet erosion have wasted the land. Now the government is trying to stop the erosion with the same conservation measures that have been used in this country. It will take years.

In South Africa the slogan for farmers is: "Plow on the contour, plant on the contour, and irrigate on the contour, if you want your children to inherit your farm."

In most parts of Africa, before the settlers came, land was held in common by the tribes, though it was sometimes divided into family plots for use. A Nigerian chief expressed the African feeling for land ownership this way: "I conceive that land belongs to a vast family of whom many are dead, few are living, and countless numbers still unborn."

A great deal is being done now, in many parts of Africa, to save the land. In Kenya, in the eastern part of Africa, the British government has set up the African Land Development Board, to help save the wasted land and keep the deserts from taking over more land. The program of the Board is not forced on anyone. People may do as they wish with their own land. But by showing them better ways of farming and herding, the Board tries to persuade people to change. Progress is slow. But in a country where the Europeans are comparative newcomers, often hated and resented by the Africans, it is better to show and persuade, patiently, year after year, than to try to force new ways.

There are many tribes in Kenya, each with its own territory which it will not let any other tribe use, even if the tribe does not need all the land itself.

The story of two tribes shows how some of the land has been used. One tribe is the Masai, who herd cattle but do not farm. The other is the Kikuyu, who are good farmers.

The Masai are a proud and ancient people who do not care for civilization or schooling or new ways of doing things. They care mainly for cattle. What a man wants most for his son is that he should walk in the dust of a bigger herd of cattle than his father's. From the Europeans, the Masai have accepted just one thing: injections to end the diseases of their cattle. But the increase in their livestock, which has resulted, is making life on their own land impossible for the Masai. The grass that has grown for hundreds of years on their wide plains is being destroyed. The Masai burn their way through the forest to find more places for grazing, but there will not forever be enough land or enough grass.

The grass can be restored, but only by keeping men and cattle off the land until nature has restored it, and then using the land and resting it in turns. To do this, people must control what they do. They must give up their freedom to have more cattle than the land can feed. The Masai have so far not been willing to change.

The Kikuyu, on the other hand, have accepted many new

ways. For hundreds of years they have been hard-working farmers, and they took reasonably good care of the land. But they have run into difficult problems.

One problem was caused by the way the land was split up by this tribe, as well as some other African tribes. A man's land, when he died, would be divided among his sons. It is the custom also for a man to have several wives, and each wife would be given a strip of land. Division of land went on and on until finally it was divided up into such small separate strips that it was impossible to keep track of them. If there were many sons and wives, still more land must be obtained for them. Land could be bought, with a payment of cattle to the owner, as long as some was available. But sometimes there was no land left that was not already in use. Then the old land might be reworked without rest. The Kikuyu themselves knew this was not good for the land.

The African Land Development Board has worked out a plan of land consolidation for the Kikuyu. The farmers of each village that accepts this plan pool their land, and it is then divided into separate farms, each in one piece. Each farmer is helped in his work by farm layouts and farm plans similar to those made by our own Soil Conservation Service.

The land of the Kikuyu is the highlands, so theirs is not a tropical agriculture. The Kikuyu farmer learns to plant in rows, use manure, plow on the contour, and rotate his crops. Most of the Kikuyu farmers like the new ways. They want to save their land. What they have done has importance for all of Africa. It has shown one way of keeping the land fertile and the deserts where they belong.

Still, the new ways have not been easy for the Kikuyu. The Europeans came to this land as strangers, not understanding the ways of the people, and often not caring. It is not surprising that the Africans would not trust them or for a long time accept any of their ways. There is more understanding now, but there is still a long way to go. The problems will not end with independence.

In his book, *Kabongo*, Richard St. Barbe Baker tells the story of a Kikuyu chief who is bewildered by the ways of the white man, whom he calls Pink Cheeks.

To Kabongo and his people, as to the American Indians, and to most Africans, the land is the mother of all the people, because to her they owe their existence. A transfer of land to a new owner, according to the old customs, involved a complicated ceremony in which the land was considered a bride to be married to the new owner.

One of the elders of Kabongo's village agreed to sell to the Pink Cheeks some land he would not need until his grandsons married. The Pink Cheeks dug the earth with a knife on a wheel, that is, a plow, pulled by an ox. The crop was good. The former owner was pleased. But when he wanted to take the land back for his grandsons, by returning what had been paid for it, the Pink Cheeks would not give it back, though this had long been the custom of the Kikuyu people. This the Kikuyus could not understand.

Land became scarce. Some of the best land had been taken by the Pink Cheeks. Many of the sons who had no land went to work for the Pink Cheeks. Too many trees were gone from the land. The ground was hot and dry.

Kabongo was bewildered. "Something has taken away the meaning of our lives," he said; "it has taken away laughter and the joy of living; above all it has taken away from us the wise way of our living in which our lives from birth to death were dedicated to Ngai [the Kikuyu god]. . . . And there is not enough land on which to feed."

The old ways on the land are changing. Not all the people

are as bewildered as Kabongo. But it is hard for a people to change so quickly the ways they have always known.

Another Kenya farmer, of another tribe, said, "What is a man without land and cattle?"

Somehow the people must learn how to keep both.

Africa's land problems are not unique. Erosion is a problem wherever sloping land is used for growing crops or for herding animals.

Much of South America has a tropical climate, like that of Africa. Farming on tropical soil there is much like farming in the African tropics. Soil is easily worn out. As in Africa, primitive people in South America and Central America grew their crops by shifting agriculture, moving from place to place as the soil they used wore out. Much of the land is still farmed in the same way today. As in Africa, and for the same reasons, this can no longer be done without destroying the fertility of the soil.

Much of the land on the broad grassy pampas to the south, in Argentina and Uruguay, has been overgrazed by cattle. In Chile, forests have been ripped or burned off mountainsides. Steep land which should never be farmed has been cleared for farming. In Peru, the soil is washing away.

In the north, on the steep hills in the uplands of Venezuela, and in other parts of the country, erosion eats deep gullies into cultivated land because most of the farmers plow their furrows up and down the slopes instead of on the contour. The modern plow exposes the South American soil to erosion as the primitive digging stick, used by farmers for centuries, never did.

Land conservation in South America is complicated by the way much of the land is owned. Enormous tracts of good land belong to landlords, most of whom do not know much about agriculture or the care of the land. What these land-lords want from their land is a good profit, every year. To bring in this profit, millions of peasants work hard on the land, growing such crops as sugar and coffee. Many never earn enough even to provide their families with sufficient food for good health.

As we have seen before, where people are used for some-one else's profit, the land is apt to be used over and over again for profit, too. And land used this way is seldom cared for well enough.

In Brazil, the government is trying to help the peasants, but it is a long slow struggle, because the landowners have much power and the illiterate peasants have little. The state of São Paulo, in Brazil, has its own land reform law.

In Brazil, too, there is a farm called Malabar-do-Brazil. There, with the help of Brazilians who do care about the land, Louis Bromfield's daughter and her husband are man-agers of a demonstration farm which shows how land can prosper when it is used with the same kind of care Louis Bromfield lavished on his Malabar Farm in Ohio.

Some of the people, and some governments, in Latin America have seen what is happening to their land. They are trying to save it. They have found that some of the abused land can never be used again at all. But some of it can be saved.

A few countries, including Brazil and Venezuela, have begun to settle landless peasants on their own land. The government of Venezuela is helping the peasants to build attractive new houses on their farms.

Land reforms are urgently needed also in Chile, Peru, and Ecuador. The restless peasants are hungry for land of their own.

Our government has set up a ten-year plan for aid to

Latin America. Under this plan, called the Alliance for Progress, the United States will help Latin American countries to develop their resources and bring a better way of life to their people. That is, the United States will help *if* these countries will make a start at much-needed reforms, such as the distribution of land to the peasants. Our government does not want to help these countries to maintain a land system in which a few wealthy families own as much as ninety per cent of the good farmland.

Work is slow. More is accomplished in some countries than in others. It is hard to teach people to use the land well, when they have no idea what this means. It is hard to change landowners who use other people to mine the land for profit. But it will be a disaster for all the people if this cannot be done.

24: The Land in India

The government of India has ambitious plans for its land. It is a country much in need of planning.

The climate of most of India is hot. The southern half of the country is in the tropics. The northern half is in the temperate zone, but it is shut off from the cool breezes of the north by some of the highest mountain ranges in the world.

Most of India depends for its very life on the monsoon rains. The more important of these rains blow in from the southwest, from June to October. This is India's rainy season.

The rainy season is followed by winter, from October to March. The weather then is like cool summer weather in our country. There is usually some rain. But in the dry season from March to June, most of the country can expect no rain at all.

Even the monsoon rain is not dependable. It may not arrive on schedule, and it varies in quantity. Some places may not have even enough rain to moisten the earth that has cracked under the hot sun. In other places, torrents of rain may fall on hills and plains that have been stripped of forests and grass. Soil washes away.

For millions of people, the behavior of the monsoon rains

has often meant the difference between having enough to eat and facing starvation.

For almost two hundred years India (including what is now Pakistan) was ruled by Great Britain. When India achieved independence in 1947, four-fifths of all the people were living in rural districts, mostly in small villages, clusters of huts made of mud, thatch, or bamboo. Most of these people were farmers. Many owned a little land which they cultivated outside the villages. But only a little. Often this land had been divided up into smaller and smaller pieces as it was handed on by fathers to their sons. A farmer almost never had enough land for a good living. Two acres was the average. Sometimes the strips of land were far apart. It was impossible to take care of them properly.

Many of the farmers were tenants on land belonging to zamindars. These zamindars were originally agents who collected rent from a certain number of villages for the government. But under British rule they were considered owners of the land. Under this system the farmers hardly had a chance. Zamindars collected from them enough money to pay rent to the government, and a big extra share for themselves. Other large landowners did the same.

The poor farmer, with too little land to start with, had to raise enough food to feed his family and sell some besides to pay his rent or taxes. He was too poor to buy good tools or any fertilizer. He plowed rather badly with his digging stick or with his wooden plow and his ox. He scattered his seed by hand, prayed for good rains, and if the rains came, he harvested his crop with a sickle. Neither he nor his family had enough energy for hard work, because none of them ever had enough to eat. The animals fared no better.

There were too many cattle, and too many of these were scrawny and useless. The Hindu religion, which is followed by a majority of the people of India, forbids slaughtering a single one of these cattle.

Wood was scarce. Forests had long since been wasted. The farmer could not afford to buy fuel for cooking, so he burned the dried manure of his cattle. It would have been better to use it to fertilize his meager fields.

Even if the farmer owned his land, he could hardly expect to improve his lot as long as he lived.

Many farmers in India still live this way. They have farmed the same way for hundreds of years. The soil has been exhausted and eroded for almost as many years.

Besides the farmers, there are millions of workers on the land who do not own or rent land at all.

There have been people who tried to help the farmers of India. We have seen how Sir Albert Howard worked out organic methods of farming in India in the early 1900s. The British government recognized the value of his work.

Sam Higginbottom was an American missionary who made it his lifework to help farmers in India to grow more and better food on their land. If he could not help them in this way, he did not see how he could help them at all.

At first, Higginbottom had trouble finding farmers who wanted to be helped. What was the use of growing more crops? they said. It would just mean more for the landlord or the tax collector. They had always been hungry. They supposed they always would be.

Nevertheless, an experimental farm was set up, and, in time, an Agricultural Institute.

On the farm, Sam Higginbottom used the same kind of plows that had been used to break up the American prairie. He needed these plows to break up hard soil that had not been plowed for years. After plowing, the earth was left rough and loose, so it could absorb the rain.

When men finally were found to work for Sam Higginbottom, they just wouldn't work well unless he was there. They would plow around the slopes while he watched. But if he stopped watching, they would plow straight up and down, as they always had before.

The men were just too tired, too undernourished, to work hard at all. Sam Higginbottom tried letting them rest for a few minutes out of every hour. He talked to them about what he hoped to do for the land. He persuaded them to try his way of farming, even if at first they were sure it was wrong. Gradually, they began to understand. More important, they began to care.

It was many years before the British government in India recognized the value of Sam Higginbottom's work. In 1932 his Agricultural Institute was made part of the University of Allahabad. Sam Higginbottom had founded it in 1910.

In time, many honors and honorary degrees came his way. He had never intended to become a farmer, but he became one of the best India has ever known.

The government of independent India is trying to create a democratic way of life for her people. Hungry people are restless. To them, a good government is simply one that helps them produce more food for themselves and their families.

This is what the government of India set out to do, in a series of Five-Year Plans for the development of the whole country. The first plan, begun in 1951, concentrated primarily on improving agriculture. The British had helped the people to cultivate millions of acres that had not grown crops before. Even so, only a little more than half of the land that could be cultivated was actually used. This was not nearly enough. There were millions more people to feed every year. Most of the land that was cultivated yielded very poor crops, thin stunted grain or poor rice. With the seasonal and uncertain rains, one crop a year was often all that could be grown.

More land must be cultivated. Two, or even three, crops a year must be grown. To do this, water must be brought to the land. Wells could not provide enough. One shallow well could irrigate only an acre and a half.

The British had seen the need for irrigation. They had installed a huge system of irrigation canals, using the water of the rivers. But nearly half of the irrigated lands went to Pakistan when it became a separate country in 1947.

The Indian government figured that about half of all the country's farm land could be irrigated. To accomplish this, dams have been built across the rivers. Water behind the dams flows into canals across the wide fields. Hydroelectric plants generate electricity. The knowledge gained by the United States in taking care of our land and planning for rivers has been of much help to India. The Damodar Valley Project is called India's TVA. Now, India has more irrigation from major projects than any other country in the world.

The agreement between India and Pakistan on sharing the water of the Indus River has helped both countries.

Water of course is essential before plants can use the fertility in the soil. But the soil itself must be fed. Indian farmers are learning to use the manure of their cows on their fields, instead of burning it as fuel. This is not easy, because fuel is necessary, too, and money to buy it is scarce.

Farmers are learning to make compost, and to grow clover and good fodder crops for their cattle. All this is learned slowly. In the past, few farmers in India have understood crop rotation or composting.

The aim of the government is to supply every acre of cultivated land with fertilizers and organic and green manures.

Forests are being restored, new forests planted. Destruction of forests has caused much of the soil erosion in India. Overgrazing and poor farming methods have caused erosion, too. In some areas, tons of soil are lost from each acre of land in the monsoon rains.

To accomplish the government's plan, the farmers, most of whom can neither read nor write, have had to be educated. Farmers who have always used metal-tipped digging sticks for digging up the earth must be shown how to use a plow. Farmers who for years have tilled their own narrow strips of land in their own way may be persuaded to pool their land with that of others in the same village, so that all the farmers can grow more food.

The First Five-Year Plan raised food production nearly twenty-five per cent. This was a good beginning. The Second Five-Year Plan was even more ambitious but did not quite meet its goals. Now the Third Five-Year Plan is under way, with increased emphasis on progress in industry as well as agriculture.

Probably the most important part of the government program for the land in India has been land reform, changing established patterns of ownership. The central government has not forced its plans for reform on the people. Instead, it has made recommendations to the separate states. Some states have carried out these recommendations more completely than others.

Part of the government plan has been to take land away from large landowners who do not live on the land, and from zamindars who control the land of small farmers and collect rent from them. The zamindars and landlords are paid for their loss of income from rents, and they are allowed to keep some land for their own use. This plan has not yet been carried out completely. Paying the landlords and zamindars is expensive. And taking away their land all at once might cause more of a social upheaval than India is as yet prepared to cope with.

Some states have limited the amount of land that may be owned by one person. Farmers who are still tenants have been guaranteed their right to stay on the land they farm. They will be more likely to take good care of their land if they are sure of keeping it. Often tenants have a chance to buy the land they farm, but few have the money to pay for it.

The government recommends, as a goal, that all land should belong to those who farm it. This makes for its best use and the prosperity of the farmers. But it will be a long time before this is accomplished in India, if it ever is. For one thing, there are too many people on the land, and millions more are born each year. Even if all the land were fairly divided, there would not be enough.

In the midst of the hurry and bustle of efficient government planning, a slender dignified man in white robes has walked along the dusty roads in India, from village to village, asking each large landowner, and even those with little land, to give a land gift, bhoodan, for the landless. This man is India's walking saint, Vinoba Bhave. When he arrives in a village, he says to the landowners, "If you had five sons, you would divide up your wealth equally among them. Treat me as your sixth son. Give me a share of your land for the sake of God and the poor." One-sixth of anyone's land is what he asks. People listen to Vinobaji, as he is affectionately called. Some wealthy landowners have contributed as much as a hundred thousand acres each. Owners of small farms have divided their few acres.

In each village, Vinobaji sets up a committee of villagers to distribute the land to the landless who need it most. He contributes his ideas. The people themselves must work them out.

This quiet man who tells the landlords that he has come to loot them with love has had great influence. He is a living expression of the responsibility of those who have toward those who have not.

The Bhoodan Yagna, Land Gifts Movement, has collected about five million acres of land and two thousand whole villages of both large and small landholders. The government has cooperated by declaring that the documents used for the transfer of land to Vinoba Bhave for the Bhoodan Yagna are legal.

Not all the land collected has been good land. Not all landowners have kept their promises. Vinoba Bhave's goal of fifty million acres has never been reached. But he has helped people all over India to accept peacefully the changes that must come, and to realize some of India's hopes for her struggling people.

"What is land?" asks Vinoba Bhave. "How is it possible for anyone to consider himself the owner of it? Like air and water, land belongs to God. To claim it for oneself alone is to oppose the very will of God."

25: Every Inch of Earth

There are places all over the world where better ways of cultivating the earth and caring for the soil are producing more food for increasing numbers of people. There are places, too, where the ways of using the land have hardly changed at all in hundreds or even thousands of years.

On the mainland of southeast Asia, the many farmers in the hills who have not changed their ways still practice shifting agriculture, burning, cultivating, and then moving on. As usual, this was not a bad system when there were few people, but now too much of the land is being worn out. Farmers are having to relearn the old South Vietnam proverb,

"Every inch of earth is an inch of gold."

In the lowlands, rice is grown on the wet broad paddies. The soil there is a rich alluvium brought down by the Mekong River and its tributaries and deposited on the land when heavy rains flood the plains. But the work is hard. Plowing with a water buffalo is slow. Each rice plant is set in the paddy by hand and tended lovingly. At last the rice is harvested, also by hand.

But in this part of the world, too, change is beginning. New ways of farming are being learned. There are plans for dams on the mighty Mekong River. When these have been built, canals will carry water across the fields in the dry season, floods will be controlled, and more food will be grown.

There are countries which have had to use almost literally every square foot of soil that could be cultivated. Either that or the people must face starvation and despair. Necessity has taught people in these countries how to take good care of their limited amount of land. They could not afford to keep the early ways that wasted the soil.

Let's take a look at some of these countries.

Japan is a country made up of four large islands and many smaller ones. There are so many steep mountains on the four largest islands that most of the land cannot be cultivated at all. And yet agriculture is the most important occupation in Japan, and more than half of the farmland is used for growing rice, usually on flat lowlands.

Miles and miles of neat careful terraces with mud-covered walls have been built around the mountain slopes in Japan. Rice is grown on these terraces. This is not easy. Rice is planted in mud and then grows under water. On the terraces, water from streams flows down from terrace to terrace. Where there are no streams, water is piped up to the highest terraces and then sent downhill. The soil on every terrace must be used over and over again and it must be kept fertile. The Japanese farmers have done this so well that they raise much more per acre than most other countries.

The Japanese farmer does all his work by hand on his own small farm. He could not get machines onto his little terraces, even if he could afford to buy them.

It was simple necessity that taught the Japanese to grow rice up the mountainsides. This is a crowded country. As the population increased, there was nowhere for the people to go. There were no great plains, like ours, no fields that had never been plowed. On islands that are mostly mountains, the mountains must be used for growing food. Japan is now trying to keep her population from growing beyond what she can provide for.

There is almost no erosion on the land in Japan. Terraces hold the water and the soil. Forests have grown for years on the steepest slopes. Lumber is cut, but a tree is planted for every one cut down. "Every inch of earth is an inch of gold."

As we have seen, land is precious in China, too. China is a much larger country than Japan, but there is not an abundance of good crop land for its bursting population. Erosion has washed away too much of the soil in northwestern parts of the country. But today, as for many centuries, Chinese farmers are fighting that erosion with long terraces built skilfully around the mountainsides.

In the south of China, canals take the water of the Yangtze River across the fields. There are rice terraces built up the hills in parts of southern China, and in the Philippines.

Earth is perhaps most precious of all in a little country called Hunza, high in the Karakoram Mountains, northwest of the Himalayas. Hunza has been part of West Pakistan since 1947, but it is so isolated, so hemmed in by high mountains, reached only by mountain trails, that it is practically independent. The people there are self-sufficient because they have to be. They depend for their living on no one but themselves.

Hunza stretches in a narrow valley along the Hunza River for about two hundred miles. It is only two miles wide at its broadest point.

A few Westerners have visited Hunza. They have come

back with tales of remarkably healthy people who have almost none of the diseases that plague the rest of the world. Some people in Hunza live to be ninety or more. It is said that the men can walk more than fifty miles in a day without feeling tired. There must be something in the way they live, and the food they eat, that makes these things possible.

These people grow their own food on soil that has been cultivated for thousands of years. They eat pretty much the same foods that are eaten in northern India and Pakistan. The difference is in how the food is grown.

The soil of Hunza is a shallow layer over rock. It is not naturally fertile. There is not very much of it. Very little of the land is flat, or even just sloping, so most of the cultivated land is terraced. Terraces are cut out of rock on the mountainsides. The walls that hold the earth on the terraces are built of stones, with the spaces between chinked with smaller stones. Soil is smoothed off behind these walls.

These terraces are quite an engineering feat in themselves, but building and maintaining them is only half the job. This is a land of little rain. All the terraces must be irrigated. Water channels and canals built with wooden shovels and ibex-horn picks bring water from glaciers on the upper slopes of the mountains. Erosion cannot even get started.

The fertility of the soil, too, is manufactured by the hard work of the people. All the organic material that comes from the land is returned to the land. All kinds of material, ashes, inedible parts of vegetables, leaves, and manure, is composted in pits, spread on the soil, and dug in. People make regular trips to different parts of the country and bring back grass or any other green growth that can be fed to their animals or distributed on the fields. There are no commercial fertilizers at all.

Two crops a year are grown. Wheat is the most important.

In the early spring, before the planting, the ruler of Hunza, the Mir, puts on a magnificent gold-brocaded gown for the seed-sowing ritual. He carries his ceremonial sword in a carved ivory scabbard. A crowd waits to see the ritual, believing that it will bring good crops. Down the field and back the Mir drives a plow pulled by two oxen, three times. Three times he sprinkles seed mixed with gold dust into the furrows he has plowed. Then he throws handfuls of seeds into the air. Anyone who can catch a seed and mix it with his own will have a fine harvest, so the people believe.

After the planting, crops are well cared for. Soil on the terraces is aerated, through the little stone walls. This helps the growth of organic material in the soil. Crops are rotated, with never the same crop on the same land twice in succession. In spite of the scarcity of land, each terrace takes its turn at lying fallow for a season, with no crop planted on it.

When the grain is harvested, the people celebrate with a dance of victory.

The Hunza way of growing crops has been called a perfect agriculture. The soil is rich with organic material because the people have made it so. Besides this, the water from the glaciers brings down silt made from rocks grinding together as the glaciers move. This silt is spread on the terraces when they are irrigated. The silt and the water itself are rich with minerals. We do not know how important these may be for the people.

The Hunzans eat the grain and vegetables from their good organic fields. They have little fuel for cooking, so much food is eaten raw and the rest cooked briefly. The good nutrients are not cooked out of it. Meat is scarce, because the Hunzans do not have enough land to grow fodder for cows and pigs. Until recently the Hunzans used a local salt which contained a variety of minerals. They drink the glacial water. They lead an active outdoor life. Perhaps we should learn more about these energetic people who live so long and so well.

Hunzans own their houses and farms. They pay no rent or taxes. Instead, they work together at maintaining the roads and irrigation canals.

So far, there have not been more people living in Hunza than the land can support. But the balance between land and people is a delicate one. No one knows what might happen if Hunza became overpopulated.

It is a long jump from Hunza in the Karakorum Range of Asia to western Europe. It is a jump not only in miles but in terms of different ways of living and different use of the land. The Hunzans grow crops to feed themselves and the comparatively few people in their country who are not farmers. In western Europe, as in most Western countries, farmers grow food primarily to sell to the many people who are not farmers, most of them city dwellers, many of them living far from the farms where the food is grown. They can buy from these other people many things they need. This pattern of interdependence is the usual one in our modern world. It is not the pattern in Hunza, where few things are bought from the outside world.

And yet there are similarities in the use of soil in western Europe and Hunza. The soil of western Europe has been used for growing crops for thousands of years, too. And the soil has been cared for, even coddled, to the point where it is probably more fertile than it was in the first place. This has meant constant enrichment of the soil with organic materials and maintaining a good balance between cropland and pasture. These soils, like those of Hunza, might be called manufactured.

Denmark is a small country in western Europe which uses every square foot of its soil carefully and well. Crops are not grown on terraces in Denmark, because all the land is lowlands and rolling hills. Most western European countries do not need terraces, though some ancient ones are still in use in southern France.

The soil is practically the only raw material Denmark has. It is not a naturally fertile soil, and yet this same soil has made Denmark a prosperous country.

The Danes have worked hard to improve their soil. They have planted millions of trees as windbreaks to keep the sand from their dunes from blowing across their farms. They have drained the swamps and cleared miles of tough shrubs off the Danish heath so more land could be used for crops and pasture.

On this land they made, the Danes planted wheat and sold it to other countries. But toward the end of the last century, wheat from the Great Plains of the United States became cheaper for these countries to buy. So the Danish farmers started feeding their grain to cows and pigs and selling their good ham, bacon, eggs, butter, and cheese.

Most Danish farmers raise both cows and pigs and the fodder they eat. They rotate their crops, with cereals, then beets and potatoes, then grass and green fodder for the cattle. This kind of rotation provides no season of rest for the land, no fallow. On such small farms, they say, the farmers cannot afford to leave any land unused. Instead, they plan carefully for the fertility of their soil. Manure from the cattle goes into the soil; commercial fertilizers, too. One crop prepares the soil for the next. So far this system has worked out well in Denmark.

There is a Danish song which says that in Denmark "few have too much and fewer still too little." Most of the Danish

farms are small enough for the farmer to do the work himself, with his family, but still big enough for him to make a
good living. No one is allowed to own more than two farms.
Big estates have gradually been bought by the government
and divided into small farms, though no one has been forced
to sell.

Farmers have joined together in groups called cooperatives. Together, they can buy farm machinery and seed,
share their knowledge of better farming methods, and build
dairies and plants for packing bacon and ham. Together,
they share their good living from the earth.

When it comes to making land, no one has ever surpassed
the Dutch. They have made good fertile farming land in
places where there did not appear to be any land at all. The
land they have reclaimed was all under water.

Long ago, the western part of what is now the Netherlands was a land of sand dunes and swamps. It seemed
hardly a fit place for anyone to live. But the people who lived
there were determined to stay. Perhaps they felt they would
be safe, in that land nobody would want, from the warring
armies that were always taking land away from somebody
else.

But this was a hazardous place to live. The sea kept breaking through the dunes. A farmer might have all his fields
flooded, and when the sea water went away it would leave
so much salt that for years the soil would hardly grow a
thing. Worse still, sometimes the sea swept the farmer's
house away. Whole villages were wiped out. Once sixty-five
villages were flooded in a single night and ten thousand
people drowned.

The Lowlanders, as they were called, were still determined to stay. This was their home; they liked it. And it was

a rich fertile soil they tilled when the sea kept away from it.

They built low walls, dikes, to keep out the sea. This was a tremendous job, and these people had just two tools: spades for digging and wheelbarrows for carrying earth. Hard experience taught them that they could save their land with these tools only if they all worked together.

Keeping out the sea was all the Dutch hoped to do for their land, until the sixteenth century. But as they grew more skilful, they thought up a still more daring plan; they would make land where there had been none at all. They drained the swamps and pumped water out of shallow fresh-water lakes, using power from windmills. The result was more fertile farmland.

The most ambitious plan of all is still being completed. This is the Zuider Zee project. The Zuider Zee was a huge salt-water bay which took up miles of space almost in the middle of the Netherlands. Now it does not exist. A dike twenty miles long, right across the opening of the bay, has closed off the Zuider Zee entirely. Much of the land behind this dike is being drained. There will be altogether more than 550 thousand acres of reclaimed land, in units called polders. This land will become the site of farms and villages. Some of the polders are already finished.

The rest of what used to be the Zuider Zee is now Lake Yssel, which stores much-needed fresh water from the Yssel River. Some of the water will find its way to the sea through sluices in the dike.

Is it worth the great cost to make new land this way? The Dutch think it is. They have more people per square mile than any other country in the world. Most of them don't want to live anywhere else. They need more land.

The Netherlands has still another great project in the

southwestern part of the country. This is the Delta Plan. The arms of the sea in the huge delta of three rivers will be closed off by dikes. It may be twenty-five years before this project is finished. Land will be reclaimed here, too, but what the Dutch want most to accomplish with their Delta Plan is to prevent forever any flood like the one which roared through those dikes in 1953. More than a thousand people drowned in that flood, and thousands of cows. Much farmland was ruined.

What do the Dutch grow on their fertile land? Bulbs, of course, including tulips; but not mostly bulbs. Most of the lowlands is grass, grazed by more than three million cattle. Dutch butter and cheese are famous.

On higher ground, wheat and other grains, and vegetables, are grown. Every square foot of farmland has to count, because there is not really very much. The Netherlands grows more wheat per acre than any other country in the world. Dairy farms have almost as high a record. Their methods of farming are much like those of the Danish farmers.

There is a French saying: "God made the earth, but the Dutch made Holland." The Dutch themselves don't want that much credit. They will stick to their own motto: "Keep your head cool and your feet dry."

The soils of Denmark and the Netherlands, and the care they are given, are typical of western Europe. What about eastern Europe? The Soviet Union occupies a large part of it, and a big northern piece of Asia, too.

The Soviet Union is enormous. But much of the land is not good for growing crops at all. It is either too cold or too dry. The black-earth region in south-central Russia, the European part of the Soviet Union, is the most productive.

The Russians have been leaders in soil science for many years. They understand what can be done with their soil. And they know that in order to feed the growing population more and more land must be used for crops.

Dams are being built across rivers. Irrigation canals cross miles of fields in areas where the farmers cannot count on enough rain. Deserts are being made to bloom.

On the wide grassy Russian steppes, much like our own plains, sod is being plowed up. Great winds cross the steppes. Once the sod is plowed up, there is wind erosion on the steppes. This could become a dust bowl, too. The Russians are using scientific planning to prevent this, not always with success.

The amount of grain and other crops grown in recent years has been disappointing. The Soviet government has drastic new plans for growing more. For one thing, the rotating of crops and grass will be given up. This will produce more in the near future, but in the long run the damage to soil fertility may reduce the amount that can be grown.

About half of the Soviet Union has very short, cool summers. The frozen tundra of northern Siberia until recently seemed an impossible place for anyone to live except Eskimos. But settlers have gone by thousands to mine coal and cut down trees from the wide forests for lumber. It is almost impossible to ship in enough food for these people. For a while it seemed just as impossible to grow any. Except for the top layer, the ground in northern Siberia stays frozen all year long. Summers are short. Fierce cold winds blow all winter.

In spite of this, farmers on the tundra are harvesting barley, wheat, rye, and oats. They eat their own potatoes, vegetables, and fruit. This has been accomplished by adapting the plants to the short growing season and stretching the season as much as possible.

To keep some warmth in the earth, windbreaks are built to provide a blanket of snow on the earth in the winter winds. Then, to make the snow melt quickly in the spring, ashes are spread over it. The dark color of the ashes absorbs the sun's rays that would only be reflected by the white snow. This can clear the fields two full weeks ahead of schedule.

One way of making plants grow faster is by soaking the seeds in water before planting. These ingenious farmers have done this, and they have found other ways of speeding up growth.

Fruit trees are pruned in such a way that their branches grow along the ground, where they can be protected from the sharp winter winds.

Even the arctic wastes, it seems, can be used to grow food for man, if there is any summer at all.

Food for people. That is one of the chief concerns of every country in the world. In the poorer countries, most of the people are busy with this single job of producing food. In the richer countries, fewer people are involved in farming, because these countries know how to produce more food on less land, using more machines and fewer people. In the poorer countries, most of the people live only on plant foods. This is because these foods come directly from the earth. Cattle and pigs and chickens, on the other hand, must feed on plants and then convert them into meat or milk. This makes meat much more expensive to produce than plants.

There are other differences. Almost half of the people in the world live in Asia, but they have only about one-sixth of the world's food. About a third of the people in the world live in North America, western Europe, and the Soviet Union, taken together. These fortunate people consume three-quarters of the food in the world.

We are not likely to have peace in the world indefinitely while such inequality exists. The millions of hungry people in the world will not be quiet forever. Civilization is running a race with hunger, and no one knows who will win.

At a conference of the United Nations Food and Agricultural Organization, in 1961, the United States Secretary of Agriculture, Orville L. Freeman, called on all the nations of the world to "mobilize their resources in a war against mankind's oldest enemy—hunger." The United States proposed the creation of an international food bank where surplus foods could be collected and distributed wherever they are needed. A Freedom from Hunger Foundation has been created to help with this.

Perhaps it will help civilization to win the race.

26: The Deserts of the World

Two questions are often asked about the deserts of the world: How can they be made more productive? And, why should anyone bother with the deserts at all?

Deserts cover almost a third of all the land on the surface of this earth. Five of the world's six inhabited continents have dry lifeless deserts. The deserts cover too much land to ignore.

There are about three billion people in the world now. In the next forty years this number will more than double to between six to seven billion. This is not just a guess. Scientists who study population trends have worked out this figure carefully. It is based on the rate at which population is increasing right now, and this is not likely to change very much.

These figures are so huge that it is hard to make them seem real. Try thinking of the increase in population this way: ten baseball teams and a coach for each, every minute.

More than half of all the people in the world today do not have enough to eat. The amount of food produced on the land will have to be more than doubled if everyone is to have enough. We are going to need the deserts.

191

The prospect of growing crops on dry deserts can seem pretty depressing. Land without water just seems dead. But to the people who work in the deserts at the problem of making them "blossom as the rose" there is nothing more exciting.

After all, some of the deserts that are dry and useless now were once made to bloom. We have seen how the desert in the valleys of the Tigris and Euphrates rivers grew food for the people, when the water of the rivers crossed the fields in long canals. People in ancient times watered the Negev in what is now part of Israel. The northern Sahara grew food for the Carthaginians and the Romans.

For a long time people thought that the climate in these areas must have changed, that these places were not deserts at all in ancient times. But now we know that the climate in most of these places was not much different in ancient times from what it is now. The difference is in what people did to the land. When they brought water to them, the deserts became gardens.

Long ago, without any of our modern tools, people knew this could be done. Isaiah said, "The desert shall rejoice, and blossom as the rose. It shall blossom abundantly, and rejoice even with joy and singing."

In our own country, today, the Imperial Valley in California is a former desert that has been made lush with the fruits of the earth because water has been brought to it. Parts of other American deserts are being watered, too.

All over the world, the dry earth of deserts is being made fertile by bringing water to it. More than a million acres have been reclaimed. But this is not much, after all. With the knowledge scientists now have, more than 200 million acres of dry soil could be irrigated without too much expense. Even this would leave nearly eight billion acres of desert in the world. Not all of these deserts can be reclaimed. Some do not have soil that can be made fertile. Some are too cold.

One challenge is the Sahara, the earth's biggest and driest desert. It is larger than the whole United States. There are more than three million dry square miles of it, from the Atlantic Ocean across Africa to the Red Sea, and a thousand miles from north to south.

Only about one-fifth of the Sahara is sand. This is the erg. Where the sand is covered with small stones and boulders, it is called the reg. There are thousands of squares miles of this, flat, dry, and dreary. The hammada is a wide rocky plateau with strange wind-whipped shapes. It looks rather like the surface of the moon. In about the middle of the Sahara sits the Hoggar, a huge mass of rocky mountains.

Sah'ra is an Arabic word meaning dull-colored, mousy. This was the name the Arabs of this region gave to their barren expanse of earth and rock.

The Arabs have a way of explaining the desert. They say that Allah, their god, wanted one place in the world where he could walk in peace. So he removed from the desert all unnecessary human and animal life. The desert is the garden of Allah.

But Allah must sometimes have grown tired of his miles of barren sand and rock, because every now and then the desert bursts into bloom.

The Sahara is not without any rain at all. There may be no rain for as long as six or seven years, then suddenly torrents burst from the sky and rush down a river bed that looks as if it had been dry for centuries. People may even drown in a sudden desert storm.

If you walked in the desert after the rain, you would hardly believe your eyes. Little green shoots would be coming up everywhere. Thousands of seeds that had been lying in the sand for years would have sprouted in the moist earth. A few days later buds would burst open and you would see miles of vivid red and yellow and blue flowers. New seeds would form a day or two later and fall to the earth, which had become dry again. There they would wait, perhaps for years, for the next rain.

These desert plants go from seed to blossom and to seed again in about a week. Flowers that do not grow this fast cannot blossom in the desert at all. But there are less colorful plants that survive here and there in the desert. These are the plants that put their roots down so deep that they find water underground. Plants no bigger than daisies may have roots twenty feet long. Tamarisk trees put their roots down a hundred feet to find water.

The Sahara sands could never have such a variety of plant life after the rain if they were just like the sand on an ocean beach. There is some of that kind of sand in the Sahara, but there are also the makings of good fertile earth. Across the wide stretches of the Sahara the wind blows a fine natural loess like that on our Great Plains. This loess carries its own possibilities for fertility. All it needs to come alive is water.

If water could be supplied continuously to this Sahara earth, plants would live and die and decay there all the time and so give organic matter to the soil. Fertility would be maintained.

For centuries, grass and shrubs and small trees grew in the river valleys of the Sahara. They held the little rain that fell and poured down these otherwise dry valleys. This helped to keep the desert from spreading. But the wandering tribes of the desert destroyed almost all this growth. They used the shrubs and little trees as fuel for their cooking. Their camels and sheep and goats ate up the grass. Today you may see nomad women in the desert searching everywhere for a shrub or a small tree. If they find one, they will pull it up or cut it down and drag it to their campfire. Every time this happens, one more plant whose roots might have held moisture in the earth is gone. There is a little more desert than there was before.

When whole forests are destroyed on the edge of the desert, there are miles of new desert. Much of the story of the Sahara is a story of vanished forests.

There is the story of Sid Tayeb, a Mohammedan miracle worker. One day he was bitten by a viper in the Forest of Guir, in what is now southern Algeria. In retaliation, he declared that this forest was his. He invited all the animals and reptiles to leave it. Then he died. The animals went away. Sid Tayeb had left the Forest of Guir to his followers. Joyous at having such a huge forest for their own, they cut it all down.

For many long years there was nothing but barren waste where once flourished the Forest of Guir. The trees of this forest had started to grow in some long-ago rainy season. Trees can grow again in the Guir only if people plant them and water them as they grow. You will read later in this chapter about how this is being done in the Guir.

Then there is the story of the Bedouins (North African Arabs) of Libya. Their country had been ruled for years by the Italians, for the benefit of Italian settlers. The Bedouins hated the Italians. When they were freed from Italian rule in World War II they celebrated by hacking down or pulling up a million trees which the Italians had planted. Again, a forest became a desert.

The nomads of the desert are used to empty sand and rock. It has taken them a long time to begin to appreciate trees. But they are learning. There is a town in Libya, Zuara, which was caught between two winds and was being buried in desert sand. Trees were planted along the dunes to stop the wind. The town officials made it a crime for people to destroy the trees themselves or let their animals chew them up. It wasn't hard for the people of Zuara to see why the trees had to stay.

There have always been people who dreamed of bringing water to the Sahara. To them it seemed that its vastness and dryness were just waiting for someone to bring it to life. They were not far wrong. There is water under that desert. When people walk across miles of dry sand, up and down the hot treeless hills of the Sahara, they are walking over a huge underground reservoir of water. This is not like reservoirs on the surface. It is more like a gigantic sandy sponge full of water. Water deep under the surface is mixed with loose sand and porous sandstone. Thousands of square miles of this reservoir, called the Albienne Nappe, stretch southward from the foothills of the Atlas Mountains.

The water in this underground reservoir comes from rain on the southern side of the Atlas Mountains. It moves southward under the desert, with only the force of gravity, in a journey that takes centuries. When a well is drilled down to this layer, the water that comes up may have been down there for thousands of years.

This water is under pressure, because it is at a lower level than the mountains it comes from. The wells that reach it are therefore called artesian. In some places water gushes out with such force that if it were not checked it would spout up in a column a thousand feet high. The water is hot, and a little salty, but it is considered good in the Sahara.

Doesn't this underground supply solve all the problems of watering the Sahara? Not quite. In most places, the Albienne Nappe lies very deep under the desert, and heavy drilling machines must be used to reach it. This is often too expensive, especially far from the coastal cities.

Then, too, it would be foolish to take more water out than is being replaced. Water is traveling into the Nappe from the mountains all the time, slowly, but no one knows as yet how much there is.

Not long ago, however, oil was discovered under the Sahara, even deeper than the water. It pays to drill that deep for oil. Oil wells mean more people living in the desert, more machines. They will need water. It will pay to drill down deep for this water. It will still be wise not to use too much.

There have always been oases in the desert, places where plants can grow and people can live because there is water. These are in the desert, but not of it. In the Sahara, the water in oases comes sometimes from rain, when the oasis is near mountains, from wells dug by hand where the underground water is not too deep, or from deep wells drilled with modern machinery. Sometimes, too, the water comes from miles of long horizontal tunnels under the desert, reaching back into the hills where there are springs or underground rivers.

Let's take a look at some of the oases in the Sahara, in Algeria.

There is Taghit, an oasis where nothing will grow except date palms, because they alone can flourish in the salty soil of Taghit. This is a lovely oasis, with green palms, a castle, and a rose-pink fortress, cradled in sand dunes. But in it the people live miserably on nothing but dates and water.

Quite different is Abadla, sixty miles west from Taghit, in the valley of the Guir, where the story says that Sid Tayeb's followers chopped down a forest. There has certainly been no forest in the Guir for a long time. Until recently this was a sun-baked desolate valley, a wadi, where torrents of rain rushed down four or five times a year and were lost in the desert sands.

Arabs had for years grown some crops in Abadla by planting their seeds after a rain, wandering off into the desert, and then returning in time to harvest what they had planted.

Now there are miles of wheat at Abadla, gardens full of flowers, trees heavy with fruit. This was made possible because French engineers discovered that what looked like solid rock in the valley was a deep layer of silt that had washed down from the mountains and been baked hard by the desert sun. Tractors were used to break up this crust. Underneath it was rich damp soil. With the crust broken up, more of the water in the occasional rains could sink into the earth.

Some of the Arabs of this region were persuaded to cultivate the valley collectively, sharing the machines and the work. Check dams have been built to control the violence of the rainstorms and send the water where it is needed. Trees are being planted in the mountains. Sid Tayeb's forest may return to the Guir, after all.

In the center of the valley is an agricultural experiment station which the French government has set up for testing and selecting the best types of plants for the valley of the Guir, and the best ways of farming there.

About three hundred miles northeast of Abadla and Taghit, still in Algeria, are two oases with the same name, Zelfana I and Zelfana II.

Zelfana I is supplied with water from an artesian well nearly four thousand feet deep. The drilling of this well proved there was water under the desert in the Albienne Nappe.

Zelfana II is also watered by wells drilled down to the Albienne Nappe. There, plots of land are given to Arabs who promise to use good conservation methods in cultivating them. Only after making such a promise is an Arab given his share of water.

In Zelfana both land and water are free. Land in the desert has no value in itself. By ancient Arab law, land on which no palms grow belongs to no one. But anyone who brings water to a piece of land, by digging a well or a ditch, owns that land.

In Zelfana, the landowner is paid by the government for cultivating the land until he has made a good start. This system could provide a good life for some of the people of the desert, who have known nothing but poverty all their lives. But most nomads do not like to stay in one place. After one good rain the desert around Zelfana turns green. The restless nomads go off into the miles of flowering dunes, to take up their wandering life until the sands are dry again.

Reclaiming the desert means more than growing forests and crops there. Most of all, it must mean bringing a better life to the people who live there and to the animals that serve them. The desert is far from empty. Wandering Arabs cross and recross it with their many camels. Small birds and animals live there. Goats travel about, chewing up the few plants that have managed to survive.

The wanderers of the desert have lived with war, hunger, and disease for many years. In Algeria, the French government prevented many wars among the Arabs and helped them to overcome disease. But this was not enough. The result was more people on the dry unyielding land, not knowing what to do with themselves. Now, some are at work in the coal mines, some at the oil wells. A few are willing to settle down to farming. When they do, they can raise some crops to sell, and grow better food for themselves.

It is not easy, though, to know what is the best way of life for these people of the desert. Certainly the choice must be their own. From their own experience and that of their ancestors for centuries before them, the nomads have learned to live in the desert, wandering over its hills and valleys, from oasis to oasis. For a long time to come this may be their choice of a way to live.

In the southwest part of Africa there is another desert, much smaller than the Sahara, the Kalahari. This is not as dry a desert as the Sahara. In parts of the Kalahari a wiry grass grows in the soft red sand. There are areas of scrubby growth, and trees here and there. In the ancient beds of rivers, which no longer flow, the soil is rich alluvium, washed down long ago when the rivers did flow. This is baked hard in the sun. There are flats where this hard surface holds the infrequent rain water for months. These flats are called pans. Without these, no animals or people could live in the Kalahari.

There are people living the primitive lives of the stone age in the depths of this desert. These are the Bushmen. They were very early people of Africa, driven into the desert by invaders who were better fighters than they.

Since they must live there, these people have adapted their lives to the desert in a way which is amazing to us who depend so much on the ways of civilization. They are wandering hunters, as was early man. The men do the hunting and bring to the campfire at night small animals, such as rabbits, or large ones, such as the gemsbok. The women gather moist roots, berries, and fruits.

There is little water available in the Kalahari until the rains come. Then the desert bursts into bloom and the pans hold water. Bushmen store water carefully in bowls which are ostrich egg shells. Sometimes when the pans look completely dry they will dig a hole and suck water up carefully through a reed from below the surface.

These people have never abused their surroundings. They have never even dug up the earth to plant a handful of seeds. Under primitive conditions, farming is impossible in the desert.

The Bushmen are a simple people living close to nature in a desert where the dry season is long and keeping alive depends on having keen wits and knowing unusual ways of finding food and water. They have learned to live together in peace, sharing whatever they have, because they must live this way to survive.

For these hunters of the desert this is a good life. Indeed, it is the only way they can really live. They have fitted their lives into the desert so completely that they seem a part of it.

But sometimes around their small fires at night they may tell tales of the days when so much of Africa was theirs.

Probably no desert in the world has ever been made to bloom as rapidly as has the Negev, in the present-day state of Israel.

The whole of Israel is smaller in area than our state of New Jersey. In this small country, only the narrow plain on the west, along the shores of the Mediterranean Sea, is naturally well-watered and fertile.

The Negev Desert is the southern part of Israel, a triangular piece of land with its southern tip on the Gulf of Akaba in the Red Sea. Before the state of Israel came into existence in 1948, the Negev was described in guide books as a true desert, scorching hot by day and cold at night. It has lowlands, a plateau, mountains and valleys. The mountains are bleak and barren, crisscrossed by wadis, dry riverbeds down which rush the occasional rains.

More than sixty years ago, Jewish settlers first began to come to Israel from all over the world. The whole country at that time looked as if it could never be transformed into a green and healthy land. There were swamps that bred mosquitoes whose bite gave people malaria. There were rocky hills with deep gullies down which the good soil had been washing in the rain for centuries. Ancient stone terraces were in ruins. Forests had been stripped off the hills.

The Negev looked most hopeless of all. But today, even the Negev has begun to bloom. This is not the first time. In ancient times this desert was a garden. The Nabataeans, especially, cultivated many miles of this desert in the centuries just before and after the coming of Christ.

Much of the soil of the Negev is a fertile loess. At the Weizmann Institute in Israel you can see an exhibit of three trays of sand from the Negev. The first tray contains just fine dry sand. The second contains sand from the same dune in the Negev, a year later. It is lumpy; it is becoming soil. The third tray, again from the same dune, contains sand gathered after still another year. It is thicker and lumpier and contains some decaying vegetable matter. This is fertile soil. It is water that has made the difference. Water, with some artificial fertilizer, was spread over this sand many times a day until it became what it had always been capable of being, good fertile soil.

Water is the key to the fertility of the Negev today, as it was in ancient times. After years of planning, a Master Water Plan has been adopted by Israel. This plan involves the use of every possible source of water before it can flow away into the Mediterranean or the Dead Sea. Water from the northern part of the Jordan River is brought to the Negev in a tremendous concrete pipe. Water is piped south from other rivers, such as the Yarkon. Even sewage water from cities is purified and used for irrigation. Someday the Mediterranean Sea may be used. This depends on finding an inexpensive enough method for taking salt out of water.

Israel has even better plans for the Jordan River, but these plans depend on the cooperation of neighboring Arab countries. So far these countries have been unwilling to cooperate, even though they need water for their own dry land, too. The Jordan Valley Plan could mean as much to this valley as the TVA does to the Tennessee River Valley in this country.

The Negev is becoming greener every year. A handful of men and women started farming there in 1943. Now there are more than a hundred farming settlements. Four crops of vegetables are grown in a year. Flowers and fruit are abundant. Birds sing in the desert. Butterflies flit among the flowers people have planted. There are bees among the blossoms.

Farmers in the Negev look to the future. They follow this motto: "Farm as if you would live forever."

All over Israel, swamps are being drained, rangelands are being planted with grass, forests are being restored to the hills. Groves of oranges grow where swamps used to be. There is twice as much cultivated land today as there was in 1948; four times as much irrigated land.

Lake Huleh was a wide swampy lake at the northern end of the Jordan River. It is not there any more. It was drained and cleaned up to make farmland. This was a tremendous job. A small wildlife preserve was kept for the exotic birds and fish that had lived in the swamp. Where most of the swampy lake used to be are now neat squares of cotton, peanuts, rice, and garden vegetables. Here is some of the richest soil in the world, fifteen thousand acres of it.

Swamps have been drained in other parts of the world, but not always so successfully. When swamps were drained for growing crops in Florida, the black muck which had looked so rich in this semi-tropical climate proved to be not so fertile after all. Tons of fertilizers had to be poured into it. Miles of swampy land have been drained in our Middle West, where no more farmland is needed, and thousands of ducks and other water birds die for lack of water.

Israel remains the bright new example in the world of what can be done to make poor land into rich land. Many people, from all over the world, have helped. People from the United States, especially. Organizations have helped, too. The Food and Agricultural Organization of the United Nations is one of these.

Sam Hamburg was an American farmer from the desert of California who introduced cotton into Israel in 1952. He was a farming missionary to Israel. Sam could tell which soil was good by the feel and the smell. He picked out a desolate spot in the Negev. This, he said, would be a good place for a farm. He brought machines, engineers, and seed from California. The Jordan River was two hundred feet below this land. Sam and his men built lifts, ditches, and canals. They pumped the water of the Jordan up two hundred and twenty feet so it could flow down into the canals across the fields. Then he taught men and women how to plant cotton, corn, peanuts, and other crops. Some of these people had been shoemakers, tailors, silversmiths; some had been beggars.

This farm was Chavat Shmuel, Sam's farm. Sam Hamburg helped to show the people what could be done in the desert.

Much of the future of Israel is in the Negev. The people are moving south into it as the American pioneers moved westward over the prairies. Israel is a small country. But its people have big ideas. They are trying to do in one generation what other countries have taken centuries to accomplish. This is the promised land of the Jewish people, and they are working hard to keep it "flowing with milk and honey."

There are of course many other deserts in the world. South America has its Atacama Desert. There are five deserts in North America. The deserts of Asia appear on the map as a continuation of the Sahara, beginning with the Arabian Desert and extending east through the great Gobi Desert in Mongolia. There are also cold deserts, the great Arctic and Antarctic wastes where it is too cold for anything to grow.

Some of these deserts are already growing food for people. Others may do so in the future, if water can be brought to them. Deserts with rivers flowing through them are the easiest to irrigate. In present-day Iraq, the valley of the Tigris and Euphrates rivers is beginning to be green again, as it was in ancient Babylonian times. The government is building dams and irrigation canals, because they know that if this desert was once good land it can become so again. Farmers are planting their seeds beside the long canals.

In their Kara Kum desert, in Asia, the Russians have changed the course of an ancient river, so that its water can flow through canals across fields where wheat is growing on land that had been dry for thousands of years.

In the past, some of the finest civilizations in the world have flourished partly because people learned how to change deserts into gardens. The future of deserts may prove to be even more important than their past.

27: Ownership of Land

Who should own the land? This question has been important to man since history began. It has not been an easy question to answer. John Ruskin said,

"God has lent us the earth for our life."

Ownership of land was not a problem in prehistoric times. It simply did not occur to early man that the earth beneath his feet could belong to anyone at all. Land was for everyone to use. Its use was a gift from the spirits who had made the world, but the land itself was given to no one.

As there came to be more and more people in the world, different groups of people, clans or tribes, would decide on boundaries for their hunting and their gatherings of the fruits of the earth. Usually they kept within these boundaries. But there might be war between the people of two clans if some of them strayed too far.

Individual land ownership began when farmers planted their fields and stayed beside them as the grain grew and ripened. A man wanted his own garden just for himself and his family. He would fight to keep other people away from it.

The division of land in those days was very simple. The

strongest man could choose the best land for his own. Those who were not good fighters would have to take whatever was left.

So we see that in early historical times ownership of land depended on force. It has depended on force through most of human history.

At the same time, there were always people who felt responsibility toward the earth, people who worshipped the earth as their mother and the source of their being. These were often the same people who had taken a piece of the land for themselves by force.

In the Book of Genesis, in the Old Testament, we read: "And the Lord God took the man, and put him into the garden of Eden, to dress it and to keep it." Man was to take good care of the earth he lived on.

In Leviticus, Moses says, speaking for God Himself: "The land shall not be sold forever [permanently]; for the land is Mine; for ye are strangers and sojourners with me."

Moses lived more than a thousand years before Christ. Already problems had arisen about the ownership of land. According to the Mosaic code, every fiftieth year was a Jubilee Year, in which all land was returned to the tribe which had originally owned it.

Psalm 25 says: "The earth is the Lord's, and the fulness thereof; the world, and they that dwell therein."

As history went on, there were many people who took for themselves more land than they should have had any right to own. Often the lands of these people were cultivated by slaves who were supposed to have no rights at all.

There were those who tried to change this inequality in the ownership of land. The Code of the Babylonian king Hammurabi stated that land could be owned only by those who cultivated it.

Solon, ruler of the ancient Greek city of Athens in the seventh century B.C., passed laws limiting the amount of land that could be held by any one person. To help the small farmers, he cancelled their mortgages, the money they owed as payment for their land. Many farmers had become slaves because they could not pay their debts. Solon freed them.

Solon's measures worked for a while, but most of the Greek rulers after him were less interested in what happened to the land and the people who worked on it.

Land ownership problems plagued ancient Rome. Hunger for land led the Romans to conquer most of the known world. A few people managed to acquire enormous amounts of Roman land for themselves. The leaders tried over and over again to limit the amount of land one man could own. They knew that the welfare of all the people depended on this. But they failed. The large landowners had too much power. They not only refused to limit their land holdings, they managed to take over most of the lands held by the government itself, and they bought out thousands of small farmers. These landless people, no longer able to get a living from the land, swarmed into the cities in discontented crowds.

We have seen how feudalism arose in the Middle Ages. The system brought some sort of order out of the confusion that followed the end of the Roman Empire. In the feudal system, most of the owners of small farms had to give up their land in return for the protection given them by the lords who owned much land.

In England, as in other feudal countries, the king was supposed to be the real owner of the land. Since the king represented the government as a whole, the idea arose that the government has a responsibility toward the land and the people on it. The land was to be used for the benefit of all,

Hillside orchard destroyed by erosion, California.

Eroded badlands in South Dakota. Land unsuited for
cultivation or grazing.

Tree roots exposed by sheet erosion in an orchard, Oregon.

Measuring the depth of soil lost from an eroded field, Ohio.

Eroded land on a tenant farm, Tennessee.

Four-horse team breaking sod with a plow, North Dakota.

Plowing in wheat stubble, leaving some on top of the
ground as a mulch, Montana.

Irrigation canal at Zelfana in the Sahara.

including the people who would live and work on it in time to come. Individual owners were not to be allowed to destroy it for any reason whatsoever.

This idea of land use was brought to America with the colonists. It was a noble concept and it remains the official policy of our government. Unfortunately, it has often been completely forgotten, both here and elsewhere.

Land ownership has too often been managed in this country not for the benefit of all the people, but for the benefit of those who could get the largest pieces of it, through having enough money to buy it or enough influence with important people to get it anyway.

Most of the colonists themselves came here because they wanted land. There had been much poverty in Europe. The old feudal system had been breaking up. Many peasants lost their rights to the land. There were a number of reasons for this. An important reason was that many pasture lands, which the peasants on a manor had shared all together, were fenced off by the lords as private sheep pastures. Thus the common lands were taken over by owners who had no right to them. These owners did not care as long as they could make money.

As in ancient Rome, the landless peasants flocked to the cities, where there was scarcely room for them all. Some became beggars. Many were hanged for stealing when they were hungry. Some came to America.

After the discovery of North America by Columbus in 1492, land on our continent was claimed by various European kings who ignored one another's claims as long as they felt it was safe to do so.

In 1493 Spain claimed all lands discovered or to be discovered on the western ocean. It was not even known how much land there was! This claim was of course impossible to maintain. The French explored the New World. So did the English, and the Portuguese. The rulers of all these countries claimed land. The claims of the Spaniards to North America were ignored by the others, except where the Spaniards had already settled.

King Henry IV of France granted the land from Philadelphia to Montreal to a Frenchman who wanted to make settlements in the New World. With considerable overlapping, James I of England granted the land from Maine to North Carolina to the Virginia Company for settlement. These claims were eventually settled by the French and Indian War. Again, land ownership was maintained by force.

Meanwhile, each European king considered the part of America claimed for his country his personal property. By merely scratching his signature on a document with a goose-quill pen, he could give away miles of this land to anyone at all.

Migration to America became a big business, in which those who had been granted land sold it to settlers at a huge profit.

It apparently did not occur to any of these kings who made grants of land in America that this land might not be theirs to give away. Yet the Indians had been living on it for hundreds, perhaps thousands, of years.

The way in which land was taken from the American Indians is a disgraceful part of our history. We have already said something about this in the chapters on early American land use and the opening up of the West. To the Indians, the earth was their mother, and they lived on this earth like good children in a mother's house.

The Indians did not sell land, because they did not understand what the Europeans meant by ownership. When you are told that Manhattan Island was sold by the Indians for only twenty-four dollars worth of trinkets, you are hearing only the Dutch side of the story. The Indians had no intention of selling this land, which they did not even feel they owned. They were willing to let the white people use it, and for this they accepted a present of gay and attractive trinkets. These two groups of people, the Indians and the Dutch, could not possibly understand each other.

The taking of Indian land by Europeans continued through the years, and the Indians fought for their land. Indians were dispossessed and moved West. Treaties were made with them giving them certain lands which should be theirs "as long as the rivers shall run and the grass shall grow." And the treaties were broken, not by Indians, but by the United States government, which did not feel bound to keep any treaty made with Indians.

Still the Indians fought back. Tecumseh was a great Indian chief who tried to unite a number of tribes in a final struggle to win back their land. Tecumseh said, "The land belongs to all for the use of each. Sell a country. . . . Why not sell the air, the clouds, and the great sea, as well as the earth? Did not the Great Spirit make them all for the use of his children?"

Perhaps Tecumseh's way of thinking is not very practical in these times. But his feeling for the land is something that can never go out of date, because it is a feeling of reverence for life itself.

The western boundary of the British colonies in North America was first set at the Pacific Ocean. When this proved impractical, the boundary was changed to the Mississippi River. Some colonies had much more land than others. After the Revolution, the states with western lands were persuaded to cede them to the national government.

This land, mostly to the west and the south, became the

public domain. It was increased by the acquisition of other large areas. The Louisiana Purchase, bought from France, almost doubled the size of this country. The Pacific Northwest was acquired by treaty with England. Later, after the end of the Mexican War in 1848, California and the Pacific Southwest were taken from Mexico.

The Federal Government was holding this land for the people. It intended to transfer most of it, as quickly as possible, to private ownership. Land was to be sold cheaply to anyone who would settle on it and use it.

This plan was supposed to prevent the grabbing of land by speculators who might buy it just for the purpose of selling it at a higher price. Unfortunately, the law did not prevent speculators from buying. Speculators and companies bought land from the government and sold it, sometimes for four times what they had paid. A congressman bought a million acres of land along the Ohio River and was later arrested for selling land that did not belong to him. One man bribed members of Congress to sell him land bordering the Great Lakes. There were other scandals.

There was a proposal in Congress that land should be sold, by law, only to those who would actually settle on it. This was obviously the sensible way to deal with the problem. It corresponded with the government's own stated policy. But the proposed law was defeated. Too many people were making money selling land, and money gave them power.

Land speculating went on and on. Speculators bought too much. Many other people could not afford to buy at all. Finally the whole situation blew up in the panic of 1836. Land values evaporated. There have been other land booms, ending in panic and confusion, about every twenty years.

Meanwhile, of course, land was also bought by homesteaders, and some went to the railroads. Some land was given to the states. A good deal still remained in the public domain.

There was plenty of protest against the misuse of public lands. It became clear that Congress would have to do something about it.

The first thing Congress did was to pass the Pre-emption Act in 1841. Penniless settlers, tired of trying to save enough money to buy land, had swarmed into the Northwest Territory and picked out a piece of land to settle down on. There were squatters in other areas, too. The land where they settled should be theirs free, they claimed. But they couldn't be sure that the land where they built their homes would ever be really theirs until the Pre-emption Act gave them the right to buy up to 160 acres of it.

The Homestead Act in 1862, as we have seen, gave 160 acres free to settlers who would cultivate it. About this time, newspaperman Horace Greeley invented the slogan, "Go West, young man, go West." Many did.

In 1862, too, the Land-Grant Act was passed. This act gave to each state thirty thousand acres of land for each senator and representative in Congress. The land was to be sold and the income used for setting up colleges of agriculture and the mechanical arts.

Two-thirds of the people's land was given away or sold. It began to look as if there might soon be no good public land left at all. There were more outcries against the waste and fraud that had accompanied the distribution of land. People had explored high mountains and lovely valleys in this country, looked into deep canyons, stood beside magnificent waterfalls. These lands, they said, should be held by the federal government forever, for the enjoyment of all the people. And so the first National Park, Yellowstone, was established in 1872.

From that time on, Congress has passed numerous laws governing the use of public lands. These lands had been used by many ranchers for the grazing of cattle and sheep. For a long time there were no rules about this at all. Too many animals roamed the range. The grass was eaten right down to the ground. The Taylor Grazing Act was passed in 1934 to regulate the use of public land for grazing. It has had limited success in this, because the working out of the law itself is controlled by the cattle owners. This act also provided for classification of public land. Land could be used only for the purposes it was classified for. This helps prevent abuse.

Cattle raisers have wanted to buy public grazing lands, so they could use them any way they liked, but there has been a public uproar against this. The lands have been kept by the government.

Public lands are managed by the Bureau of Land Management, in the Department of the Interior.

Some land laws have become badly out of date. There was, for example, a mining law which dated back to 1872. Under this law, which had been passed to help prospectors for gold and other minerals, any citizen of the United States could file a claim to a twenty-acre tract on any piece of public land. The claim must be based on the discovery of minerals on the land, enough so it would pay to mine them. But the citizen would not have to prove the minerals were there before he claimed the land. He could hold it at least until the government proved the minerals weren't there. And the government men were too busy to come around right away.

To show how this worked out, *Collier's Magazine* in 1953 sent writer Bill Davidson out to Colorado, where he placed a mining claim for twenty acres in a beautiful national forest. He paid $1.25 for recording the claim. That's all. As long as *Collier's* held the land, no one could use the timber on it. (The claimant couldn't, either; he could only mine minerals.) *Collier's* could keep everyone else off it. The government had been planning to build a section of the new U.S. Highway 6 right through the land that was taken for this claim. *Collier's* could have stopped them from doing it, at least temporarily.

Actually, all *Collier's* did was to give the land back to the government. They had proved their point.

Amendments to the mining law in 1955 straightened out some of the worst complications.

Our public lands are a precious heritage belonging to us all. It is up to the people of this country to see to it that the government takes good care of this land, which still amounts to more than four hundred million acres, about the same area, altogether, as two states of Texas, or four Californias.

What are the public lands, today? Very little of this land is good agricultural land. That was given or sold to farmers. Except for post offices and other government buildings, the public land does not include city property.

Our public lands are forest, mountains, desert, range, and swamps, ninety per cent of it in the western part of our country. Some of this land includes what may soon be our last areas of real wilderness. You will read about this in another chapter.

All over the world, restless people are demanding a right to the use of the land. People who have never owned land are hoping that a little piece of the earth may become theirs, after all. This is so much a part of the story of land, and especially the agricultural use of land, that it has been included in a number of chapters in this book. We have seen

how the Kikuyu in Africa have tried to deal with their problems. The unrest of poor farmers in Brazil, working long
hours for landlords who own enormous tracts of land, is typical of farmers anywhere in the world who live under a land
system much like the feudalism of the Middle Ages.

In most of the Middle East, the land ownership system
follows a feudal pattern. The way of life of the people has
changed very little in thousands of years.

Iran is a country where the government is trying to change
this system. Landlords have owned and controlled much of
the land there for centuries. They own whole villages, with
all the fields and houses in them. The peasants work from
dawn to dusk on the land and often receive as a reward
only a fifth of the poor crops they grow with their ancient
methods on worn-out soil. The landlords themselves often do
not live there at all. The Iranian House of Representatives in
1960 passed a land reform bill which was supposed to divide
up the large landholdings of the landlords among the peasants. The Shah of Iran set an example by giving away much
of his own land. Land owned by the state was to be
distributed.

Some peasants in Iran now do own land. Some have joined
together in cooperatives, for better farming. But progress has
been slow. It has not been easy for the government to force
the powerful landlords to give up their land. The peasants
must be taught to use their land well. But they will not be
willing to wait forever. They have heard rumors of new ways
in the world. They have heard that in other countries peasants who never owned an inch of land in their lives now
cultivate their own farms.

In 1962 the government of Iran passed another, more
drastic, land reform law that would force all landlords who
own more than one village to divide up their land, except

one village, among the peasants. This time they will have no choice. The peasants will pay for the land, in small installments. The landlords will be paid by the government. The peasants of Iran may not have to wait much longer.

In India, the slight tall figure of Vinoba Bhave still walks across the land, telling the landlords to give land to the landless.

Giving or selling a piece of land to every farmer will not in itself solve any problems. The piece of land must be big enough to be profitable. The farmer must know how to keep his soil productive and care enough to do it. He must have the right tools. Without all this—and this is often lacking—the waste of land and of human labor is enormous. Waste of people is even more important than waste of the soil. It is surprising how often the two go together.

Land that is rented may be treated well, too. Tenancy is not always bad for the land. Many well cared for farms in western Europe have been farmed by tenants for hundreds of years. The important thing is that the farmer should not pay too much of his income in rent, and he should be assured by law that he can stay on the land as long as he uses it well. If these conditions are fulfilled, both farmer and land may do as well as if he owned the land.

Some countries, such as Russia and China, have taken land from large landowners by force, without paying them for it, and have then given it to the peasants or organized it as collective farms, owned by the state and worked by groups of farmers. In Russia, the peasants have done a better job of growing crops in their own back yards than they have on the land of the collective farms. This has become quite a problem for the government.

There are farms in Israel, called Kibbutzim, where the land and everything on it is owned by all the people who live and work there together. But this way of owning land was not imposed by force. It was the choice of the people who live there.

The way of the Kibbutz might not be the choice of most people in the world today. But we are a long way from knowing what is the best way for the land to be owned and cared for everywhere. We cannot divide all the land up among all the people. Injustices in the use of the land in most parts of the world must be worked out in other ways. We want personal freedom for everyone. We want the land to be well cared for, too. These two things do not always go together.

The ancient Incas cared for their land perfectly, but they sacrificed for it their individual freedom.

The United States has given much freedom to its people, and the land has been worn out, washed and blown away. We have sprawled our cities untidily over the landscape.

The owners of land will have to accept their responsibility for taking care of it. Somehow a balance must be found between the freedom of individuals and the control of our government over the land they own.

28: Other Uses of Land

Our cities are built on land, too. When you walk on city pavements, you are walking over earth that could once grow grass and flowers. You may be walking where a forest of trees once reached toward the sky. The chances are that none of this earth hidden under asphalt and concrete will ever grow anything again. Yet much of it was good fertile earth.

A road may not look as if it takes up much space. It's just a long thin ribbon winding across the countryside. But over twenty million acres of land in our country are now covered with asphalt, concrete, and similar materials. This includes city streets, parking lots, playgrounds, and so on. A considerable part of it is cross-country roads. Our new interstate highway system will take another million and a half acres.

Cities have many problems in their use of land, and these are very different from land problems in open country. This book is mostly about agricultural land use. We will mention only a few of the problems of land use in cities.

One big problem in city use of land is how to keep some of it open and green. Every city needs parks. But there are always some people who would rather put up a building, or make a parking lot, on any land that remains green. They can make money that way. So parks have been kept green by the city governments, supported by the great numbers of people who want a place to sit in the shade of a tree, a brook to walk beside, or a little vale where the birds sing.

As more and more people have settled in cities, many parks have been bulldozed away. There are few parks left in Los Angeles. Buildings and roads have taken the place of those that have gone. In San Francisco, the state planned a wide freeway through Golden Gate Park, in the heart of the city. The manager of the Recreation and Park Department went into action. "This city," he stated, "can remain desirable or become a dump." The people of San Francisco did not want their city to become a dump. Their protest against the freeway was tremendous. It was finally built *under* the park, in a tunnel, instead of on the surface.

Outside of our cities, the suburbs are expanding into untidy groups of houses and shopping centers sprawled over the landscape. Land prices are soaring. It has been said that our cities are not expanding at their edges, they are "disintegrating and spreading the pieces over miles and miles of countryside." This is called urban sprawl.

Californians who are disturbed by what is happening as their cities expand are determined to fight against the conversion of their state into what they call slurbs. By this they mean "our sloppy, sleazy, slovenly, slipshod semi-cities."

There has been a proposal to set aside an area of green land in New Jersey, halfway between Philadelphia and New York City, before the suburbs of these two cities meet and merge.

Many people seem to think the trouble is a shortage of land. It isn't. The trouble is a shortage of good planning.

There is plenty of land going to waste on the outskirts of cities and even in the cities themselves. Look around you sometime when you are walking or driving through the outskirts of a city. You will see dozens of untidy empty lots, full of weeds and broken bottles, dumps and automobile graveyards, wasted space between buildings. Much of this land may be useless as it now stands. Better planning could have saved it.

Planning is just as necessary as you move farther out. Practically all of the land that is going to be used for developments, new houses and schools, shopping centers and so on, belongs to individuals, or sometimes to groups of people. They naturally want to make a profit when they sell. If the land they own is quite near the city, they may decide to hold on to it until prices go up. The developer, wanting cheaper land, will skip that land and build his houses farther out. In this way, developments spring up here and there, wherever it seems easiest to get land.

Another thing. Most developers want good flat land, easy to build on. This is apt to be Class A land, good for farming, too. Good for parks. Actually, with very little additional expense, the developers could build on hilly land, even on rocky land. Builders can put up houses in the midst of trees, instead of bulldozing down the trees. The results of this kind of building are much more interesting than rows of houses sitting just the same way on long flat streets.

The land that is left between developments is usually not parks. It may be farmland. Or it may be just empty land someone is holding in hopes of making money. In that case it may be overrun with weeds and brush. It may be littered with tin cans. You might call it a dump.

All this is hard on farmers in the area who would rather farm than sell their land at all. A farmer isn't likely to improve his land if he thinks he may be practically forced to sell it when he is surrounded with developments and he is offered so much money for the land that it doesn't pay him to turn it down.

So, in little bits here and there, the suburbs sprawl.

Planning by government agencies is needed, for whole areas, so that developments will be built in an orderly way, pleasant to see and to live in. Open land, with grass and trees and even here and there a brook, should be left between developments. This should not be just haphazard open land, empty lots, cow pastures where houses should be. The open land near cities should be planned for the use of the people. A private estate near a city, all neatly mowed and fenced in, is open space, but only the owner can use it. The same estate converted to a state park can be just as neatly mowed, but it is open to all the people, for their enjoyment.

How can such planning be done? It is complicated, but there are ways of planning developments so that land will be used well and there will still be open spaces.

The state, or a city, may buy land for parks from private owners. When an owner is unwilling to sell, the public, through the government, can acquire his property through the right of eminent domain, if this will serve a public purpose and the owner is paid a fair price. Land is often acquired this way for roads or for public buildings.

Another way of planning is by zoning. Zoning laws prescribe that certain pieces of land may be used only for certain purposes, such as housing, industry, farming, no matter who owns them. This kind of planning can keep houses in the right places, green spaces in between, stores and factories where they should be. In practice, zoning doesn't always work out as nicely as all this, but it is a good tool.

Most big cities have had zoning laws for many years. Colonial towns had such laws as early as 1692. Zoning is a somewhat newer idea for larger areas outside the cities.

Another way of keeping open green spaces between developments is by the use of easements. This is a legal term. Under an easement law, a community can take away from a landowner, by paying him, his right to use his land for a housing development or for any purpose (such as putting up billboards) which will make the land less desirable, less scenic. The land can still be used by the owner for farming or any other way that doesn't spoil it. The money paid to him is usually in the form of a reduction of taxes, and he is free to accept the arrangement or turn it down.

The advantage of easements is that some land is left green and open in the midst of buildings. But there are disadvantages. An easement that provides for a private golf course benefits only a few people. The same is true of an estate, or a farm. Land for these uses should be located farther out, beyond the housebuilding area. Green spaces between developments should be public parks.

Let's see how this problem has been working out in California, the first state to pass an open-space law in 1959. Monterey County has put this law into practice. It is voluntary. Landowners who decide to accept the easements provided for by the law must agree never to sell their land for housing or shopping or industrial developments. So far, only a few landowners have decided to cooperate. They are paid, yes. But it is not easy to give up the possibility of making even more money on the sale of this land later on. Not every landowner is that interested in the good of the community.

The picture throughout the country is not all bad, however. Some very good planning is being done. Dozens of new communities are being built with open green parks and a variety of houses. This kind of planning is turning out to be more practical than most builders ever thought it could be. In time, most new communities may be built this way, and not just for the people with the most money. But dozens are not enough. Much more of this kind of planning needs to be done.

There are state programs, too. Wisconsin has a broad plan for preserving large areas of lovely countryside before they are taken over for industry or housing. New Jersey has its green acres plan. New York State is acquiring land for more state parks. Some public land is being turned over to the states by the federal government for parks.

Another complicated question is that of taxation of land. Take open land near cities, for example. Should the tax on this land be high or low? When the tax is low, the owner can afford to hold onto it until he can sell it for as high a price as possible. He may keep the land green for a while, or even use it for public recreation. But since he expects to sell it at any time, he is more likely just to let someone put up a hot-dog stand on one corner of the land, or make an untidy parking lot out of it, or a dump. When he sells the land, someone else will have to clean it up.

If the tax on this land is kept high, the owner is more likely to sell it when that area is being developed in the way that is best for that particular piece of land.

The taxation and renting of land has been a difficult and controversial question from the first.

The American economist and philosopher, Henry George, was much concerned with problems of land ownership and taxation in the last half of the nineteenth century. It seemed to him that there was nothing more necessary for the life of every human being than land. "What would man be without land?" he asked.

Land is not just a place to raise wheat or graze cattle and sheep. None of us could live without it. We all occupy land, even if it is only a half acre of cement poured over the earth. Our daily lives depend on people who work on or under the earth—the farmers, the ranchers, the miners, the lumbermen, the oilmen, and all those who bring the necessities of life to us on miles of roads and rails over the land.

The land should belong to everyone, Henry George said. It belongs by right to society itself. He was not entirely alone in this view. The Indians would have understood. And Abraham Lincoln had said: "The land, the earth God gave to man for his home, sustenance, and support, should never be the possession of any man, corporation, society, or unfriendly government, any more than the air or water. . . ."

Henry George felt that inequality in the ownership of land was the greatest single cause of poverty in the world. It was wrong for a few people to have huge amounts of land, while many had none at all. George knew how miserable people could be when they lived in poverty, because he had been poor himself. He wanted to do what he could to help.

The remedy for poverty, Henry George said, was to give all people equal rights to the land. He did not, however, urge that the land should be taken away from its owners and divided up among all the people. That would be entirely impractical in our complicated civilization. What people want, in any case, is not necessarily ownership of the land itself. They want to be sure of owning whatever they produce on the land.

Henry George did not say, either, that all the land should belong to the government. Instead, he urged that the value of the land, that is, income from the land, should be shared by all the people. This would be done by taxation. The land, and according to Henry George, only the land, would be taxed on its full value, as it seldom is now. This would be the equivalent of landowners paying rent for land to the government, as representative of the people, as if the land were common property. The taxes from land would then be used for the benefit of everyone.

To Henry George it seemed all wrong for anyone to make money just by selling land, or renting it, when he hadn't done any work whatsoever for the money. George lived at a time when speculators were making enormous sums of money by buying and selling land in the West.

It would not be practical today to abolish all taxes everywhere except those on land. This has not often been done. But the general idea of land-value taxation has taken hold in a number of places around the world.

The main idea of land-value taxation, as it has developed, is that land should be taxed, but not the buildings and other improvements on the land. Or at least, the land should be taxed at a much higher rate than the buildings.

Under most present laws, an empty lot in the city which is doing nothing but growing weeds and collecting rubbish carries a low tax rate compared to the lot next to it with an apartment house on it. The empty lot doesn't seem worth much, because the owner isn't getting any money out of it. The owner of the apartment house, however, must pay a higher total tax on both land and building, because he *is* making money from his property. If he improves his apartment house, his taxes on it will go up still more, on the theory that he will be making more money.

This sounds very logical and seems so to many tax experts. But let's see what often happens. The man with the empty lot hesitates to build anything on it, because then the taxes will take so much of his profit. The man with the apartment house on the next lot hesitates to improve his apartment house, for the same reason. Neither property is improved. This kind of thing is happening all the time in our cities.

Slums remain slums, often because the owners are making a tidy profit and might not do as well if they improved their buildings and so had their taxes considerably raised. The result would be different if only the land were taxed, on the basis of the best possible use that could be made of it, or if it were taxed at a higher rate than the buildings. If this were true, the owner of the empty lot could not afford to leave it empty, just wasted. The owner of the apartment house would feel like improving it.

In the United States, a number of communities have been organized around the idea of land-value taxation. The two largest of these are Fairhope, Alabama, and Arden, Delaware. Fairhope was founded in 1895, on the shores of Mobile Bay. Land in Fairhope became the property of the Fairhope Single Tax Corporation. Lots were leased to people for ninety-nine years and rent for the land was collected and used as the only source of funds for social services and public improvements. This has proven to be more than enough. The town has grown and prospered. Everyone shares equally in the value of the land.

Arden has followed a similar pattern.

In the cities of Pittsburgh and Scranton, Pennsylvania, the tax rate on land is twice as high as the tax rate on buildings on the land.

In Australia and New Zealand, many cities have been taking most, sometimes all, of the tax off buildings and raising the tax on land. The result is that owners of good houses find that their taxes go down, because the houses are not taxed any more. Owners of poor or run-down houses find that their taxes are raised, because the land is now taxed in terms of its best possible use. It doesn't pay to own run-down houses.

In Great Britain, on the other hand, land which is not in use is not taxed at all.

Denmark was the first country in Europe to emphasize the tax on land values, as a national policy.

The government of Jamaica, West Indies, has put out a helpful booklet, explaining to the people its new land-valuation law, passed in 1956. This booklet makes it clear that buildings are not the only improvements on the land. The booklet states, in part:

"Land in a town or near a town is worth more than land in the bush. . . . Good land is worth more than bad land. But anything else on the land—houses, trees, crops, soil-conservation works, anything whatever that has been done by man for the purpose of improving land and increasing its value— will not be taxed as land. That is man's labor, and he will not be taxed on his labor.

"Put anything on your land. Under the law, only the raw land will be taxed."

This is the land we live on. We owe something to society for the use of any piece of land we call our own.

29: Land Forever Wild

In May of 1950 the United States Forest Service held a public hearing at Riverside, California. The subject of the hearing was a proposal to build a tramway to the top of nearby Mount San Jacinto. Feelings of people at the hearing ran high. Those who wanted the tramway were sure they were right. Those who didn't want it were just as sure.

Why all this fuss about a tramway up a mountain?

The company that wanted to build the tramway planned to turn the top of the mountain into a popular resort, with all sorts of amusements. People would love it, they said. The company would make lots of money. To carry out this plan, they would have to build a tramway up the mountain. Why shouldn't they build it?

A surprising number of people were absolutely against anyone's building such a tramway. The top of Mount San Jacinto had for some time been a state park, kept as a nature sanctuary. A good part of this would be completely spoiled by the building of a resort. The tramway itself would have to cross a small piece of National Forest, and that would be changed forever. This is what the hearing was about.

Conservationists came from all over the country to speak

in favor of leaving the mountain untouched. People who were more interested in making money than in saving wild places spoke emphatically in favor of building the tramway and the resort. It was a day of heated arguments.

Toward the end of the day an elderly woman came forward to give her opinion. She was too old to climb mountains, she said. She would never see the top of Mount San Jacinto. But she thought that this mountain, and others, should be left unspoiled for those who could climb and who needed a wild place on a mountaintop.

It was enough for this woman to know that the wild places were there so that people in the years ahead could enjoy them. She has not been alone in this feeling. In recent years, more and more people have spoken up for the preservation of wilderness areas.

What do we mean by wilderness? And why should any of it be preserved?

Wilderness is a place that has remained just as nature made it, unchanged by man. The wonderful interrelated processes of nature are going on there all the time, undisturbed. Man does not change a wild place if he goes there quietly, not roaring over trails in a motorcycle or across lakes in motorboats, but going on foot or on horseback along trails which hardly disturb the wildness on each side. Roads for automobiles have no place in wilderness.

Strictly speaking, to be considered wilderness an area must be a hundred thousand acres or more in size, large enough so that its wildness is not affected by the areas next to it. An area of from a hundred thousand down to five thousand acres is called a wild area. The largest wilderness area under the United States flag is in Alaska. Most of the remaining wilderness in this country is in the Rocky Mountains and to the west of them.

But why go to the wilderness at all? Some people never do want to go there. They would only be uncomfortable in the wilderness. But for others there is adventure in climbing high mountains and finding their way through wild forests. And this is not all. In wilderness people may find a better understanding of themselves and their place in nature. They can feel at peace with themselves as they look across wide far lakes where the only ripple is that made by a falling leaf or the quiet swimming of a wild duck.

If you went from the city to the wilderness in the Sierra Nevada, or other mountains, you would first fill your eyes with the magnificence of pointed peaks against the sky, wild streams and waterfalls tumbling through rocky canyons. Then, when you had been there longer, you would learn to listen. You would hear the murmur of pine needles blown against each other in the wind. Through the branches above you would come the clear notes of a white-throated sparrow. In the quiet that followed you could hear the small persistent sound of little insects at work in the leaves beside your feet.

You might not have noticed these things before. You might not have cared. But there is excitement in discovering them for yourself.

You would not find it easy to put this experience into words. And not everyone would understand.

In California's Point Lobos State Park, not many years ago, a woman was discovered busily pulling up plants beside a path with both hands. She said she was helping clean up the place. She was one of those who do not understand.

Others, who might understand, do not care. But there must be unspoiled wilderness left in the world forever for those who do care.

It does not matter if only a few people are in the wilderness at any one time. There are not often crowds of people in art galleries, but this does not mean that we should not have art galleries.

It does not matter, either, if the people who use the wilderness just feel they like camping, without being philosophical about what it does for them. There is room for many ways of enjoying wilderness, as long as it is left unchanged.

This respect for natural wilderness and the creatures in it is rather a new thing in the world. One of the things that makes man most different from other beings on this earth, and often superior to them, is his ability to change his natural surroundings. This ability has produced our fine buildings, our roads and railroads, our huge dams, miles of irrigation canals, and much more. But throughout history man has determined also to conquer nature. He has worked at this when it brought a better life to people and when it did not. Now he has it in his power to all but do away with nature entirely. He can decide to keep some of the wilderness or to destroy it all. And he is beginning to want to keep it.

When the Pilgrims landed in New England, they could see before them nothing but a desolate wilderness which they would have to subdue. Throughout the early history of this country, wilderness was considered an enemy of man. It must be gotten out of the way. Only the timber and the gold and the soil in fertile valleys and on the wide plains was considered of any use to man. Animals in the woods were good often to eat, often for furs, but not just for themselves.

When the West was opened up, there were plenty of people who thought that most of the land there was worthless. The statesman Daniel Webster said: "What do we want with this vast worthless area, this region of savages and wild beasts, of shifting sands and whirlwinds of dust, of cactus and prairie dogs? To what use could we ever put these great deserts or endless mountain ranges . . . ?"

To Webster, as to some people even today, land was without value unless it had a practical use.

Feeling about the wilderness has changed in this country as the amount of it remaining has grown smaller and smaller. As more people crowd into our huge cities, more and more feel the need to get out, at least occasionally, into wild quiet places far from the cities. There is a growing interest in the idea of saving at least some of the wilderness we have left, and the creatures that live in it who may disappear from the earth forever if nothing is done.

The story of the passenger pigeon shows how easily a creature can become extinct. In 1857 a committee reported to the Ohio State Senate on the possible need for protection of the much-hunted passenger pigeon. The committee had concluded that no protection was needed at all. There were so many of the pigeons that their flights hid the sun as they passed. They had the vast forests of the north for the raising of young. They could travel hundreds of miles a day in search of food. Many were killed by hunters, but, the committee said, they would never be missed among the myriads that were produced each year.

The killing went on. Efforts were finally made to save the pigeons, when it was too late. On September 1, 1914, Martha, the last passenger pigeon to exist anywhere in the world, died at the age of twenty-nine years, at the Cincinnati Zoological Garden. There will never be another. You may see the remains of Martha, stuffed, at the National Museum in Washington, D.C.

We cannot take it for granted that wilderness will remain forever if we do nothing about it. But there is a difference now in the attitude of many people in the world. The well-known naturalist Aldo Leopold said, in his speech at the dedication of a monument to the extinct passenger pigeon, in Wisconsin, 1947:

"For one species to mourn the death of another is a new thing under the sun. The Cro-Magnon who slew the last mammoth thought only of steaks. The sportsman who shot the last pigeon thought only of his prowess. The sailor who clubbed the last auk thought of nothing at all. But we, who have lost our pigeons, mourn the loss. Had the funeral been ours, the pigeons would hardly have mourned us."

The destruction of one natural species may upset the entire natural chain of life in ways we do not completely understand.

The act of Congress which set aside a wilderness area in Wyoming as Yellowstone National Park stated that this land was "dedicated and set apart as a public park or pleasuring-ground for the benefit and enjoyment of the people." All natural features of the park were to be kept unspoiled. This was the first national park anywhere in the world. Since that time, there have been national parks set up in many other countries. Canada has eighteen great national parks, just to the north of us. These contain many acres of wilderness.

Yellowstone is still our largest national park, more than two million acres, two-thirds the size of the state of Connecticut. It is significant that the *whole* wilderness of Yellowstone was set aside, not just a spectacular geyser, a canyon, or a waterfall. Broad tracts of wilderness were to be part of the heritage of the American people.

The National Park Service Act of 1916 established the National Park Service, to care for all the parks and plan their use. The Service was to "conserve the scenery and the natural and historic objects and wildlife therein and to provide for the enjoyment of the same in such manner and by such means as will leave them unimpaired for the enjoyment of future generations." The same purpose was to be applied to National Monuments, which are areas set aside primarily for their scientific and aesthetic interest.

The wilderness is there, in our national parks, even if most park visitors do not explore more than a few miles beyond their lodge or camping ground. It is there for those who do want to explore the trails that lead deep into its woods and paddle canoes down its wild streams.

It has by no means always been easy for the National Park Service to keep the parks "unimpaired for the enjoyment of future generations." There have been attempts by a number of groups of people, sometimes powerful and well organized, to invade the parks for mining, for grazing, or for hunting the abundance of wild animals. The National Park Service has resisted. They have not had to resist alone. Numerous private citizens, organizations, and congressional leaders have helped.

There have been, too, some rather strange proposals from people who cannot understand what parks are for. Someone, for instance, will want to build a summer theater in a park, a miniature golf course, a bowling alley, a summer home. All these things are fine in their place, but they don't belong in a national park.

A few years ago a group of people started up one of the trails of Sequoia National Park in California on motorcycles. They were caught by the ranger, and he made them park the motorcycles, take them apart, and carry out the pieces by horseback. They would have to do their motorcycling somewhere else.

The most recent major problem of the Park Service is one its founders could not have foreseen. Preservation of the parks has come to mean protection against too much use by people, even the right kind of use. So many people have been visiting the parks that providing for them all has become a tremendous task. All of these people are entitled to have some experience with the wilderness in the parks, but too many camping and tramping about may change the wilderness completely.

To cope with this problem and other problems of park management, the National Park Service has launched an impressive new plan called Mission 66. Conservationists feel that the wild character of parts of some parks has been spoiled by recent changes made under this plan. Broader highways in parks, and still more villages where people can stay overnight, make it almost impossible to keep the parks "unimpaired for the enjoyment of future generations." The remoteness and quietness which belong to an experience of wilderness are lost.

The number of national parks increased from one to twenty-nine between 1872 and 1960. Two of these, Platt and Hot Springs, do not fully meet the requirements of a national park. Between 1950 and 1960 there was only one new national park, Virgin Islands National Park. Now there are proposals for making a number of others. There is a growing feeling among many people in this country that this must be done before it is too late. One of the proposed parks is Prairie National Park in northeastern Kansas. The soil of our prairies was the richest in our country, and very little of it escaped being turned over by the plow. But in a Prairie National Park a remaining area of grassland could be saved. Herds of bison and elk and antelope might roam the wild range again.

The twenty-six national parks that have been described as national primeval parks include more than thirteen million wild acres. There is a smaller area in wildlife refuges managed by the United States Fish and Wildlife Service. The largest combined area of wilderness, over fourteen million acres in eighty-three tracts, is in our National Forests.

The National Forests were established under the leadership of President Theodore Roosevelt and Gifford Pinchot, who became his chief forester. Theodore Roosevelt has been called "a man with distance in his eyes."

Both these men helped to make conservation a popular cause in the early 1900s. But their purpose in conservation of forests was to insure an abundance of timber for practical use. This was an advanced idea at the time, when trees were being ruthlessly torn off mountainsides without being replaced. The idea of keeping parts of the forests without any so-called practical use, as wilderness, came somewhat later, in the 1920s, under the leadership of the forester and naturalist Aldo Leopold.

The National Forests as a whole are now managed under a program called Operation Multiple Use. This means that these public lands are to be used by the people for recreation and also for such practical purposes as lumbering, grazing, mining, and as a source of water. On any one tract of land, one use is of first importance; the other uses must fit in with this. Forests that are cut for timber are managed so that trees cut down are replaced by new growth. Grazing areas are supposed to be protected from too much use, but there is still much overgrazing.

The wilderness areas are not for multiple use. These areas are to be kept in their natural state, with only the least possible change by man as he travels through.

There are people who think that lumbering and grazing should be allowed in the wilderness, too. They complain that these areas are not being used at all. This is not true.

Wilderness areas are not storehouses of lumber or water power. No one is making money from them. But wilderness is being used, for the delight of the people who go there.

Until recently, an area could be designated as wilderness by the Service that managed it. It could be changed to another use just as easily. It was hard, sometimes, to resist the pressure of groups of people who wanted to do lumbering or mining or grazing there.

This is why the Wilderness Act was drawn up and presented to Congress, to establish a National Wilderness Preservation System. For the first time, preservation of wilderness was to be a national policy, written into law. No new land would be added to wilderness areas, no new agency or bureau would be created. The total area involved is only about two per cent of the continental United States, only five per cent of all the land now held by the federal government. Put together, this would about equal in size the state of Illinois.

You might think an act like this would be easy to pass. It wasn't. Lumbermen want the wilderness areas to be available for their use. They say they have learned to use any forest area carefully, making sure there are always new trees. This is by no means always true. And a wilderness with even a few of its trees cut down and hauled out for lumber is no longer wilderness.

Mining companies have raised strenuous objections to the Wilderness Act, in spite of the fact that mining is to be allowed on these lands if valuable minerals are found there and mining them can be proven to be in the best interests of this country.

People who favor the Wilderness Act have been called snobs, a select few who want to grab some of the public land for themselves. But they do not want it just for themselves.

They hope that other people will enjoy the wilderness, too.
This land belongs to all the people. The lumber companies
and the mining companies are themselves a minority of the
American people.

The Congress of the United States found that the people
who believe in saving the wilderness are not so few after all.
Support for the Wilderness Act was tremendous. The Senate
passed the act in 1961. It came before the House of Representatives in 1962. Passage was not certain.

Wilderness is defined in this act as "an area where the
earth and its community of life are untrammeled by man,
where man himself is a visitor who does not remain."

Earth does not exist only for man's use. Eager as many
people are to find a practical use, or a price in dollars, for
everything under the sun, nature's wild trees and bushes and
grasses, and all the wild creatures of the world, have their
own reasons for being.

But if we must have usefulness, the wilderness is not
without that, too. Our natural resources have been called "a
great reservoir from which we all evolved."

Wilderness for the scientist is a fascinating laboratory for
the study of natural processes. Ecology can be studied there
in a way it cannot possibly be in a laboratory built by man.
Scientists can often tell what to expect of sick land only by
comparing it with wilderness, which is healthy land.

Wilderness once gone is gone forever. Man cannot bring
it back, though if it is not too damaged he may allow it to
restore itself. But this takes a long time.

Even with the Wilderness Act passed, it will not be easy
to make sure that generations of people in the future will be
free to explore the far wild places of the earth. There are
still those who would whittle it away, little by little.

The conservationists are well organized now. The Sierra

Club, founded by naturalist John Muir in 1892, was the first organization to work primarily for the conservation of wilderness in this country. It now has about twenty thousand members. Other organizations are on the alert, watching to see what happens to the wild places and the wild animals and birds of this country. Among these are The National Audubon Society, The Wilderness Society, the American Wildlife Federation, The Izaac Walton League.

It is important for people to know to whom they should write in Congress, when they think laws about conservation should be passed. *National Wildlands News,* published in Washington, D.C., brings this information to people, as well as information about happenings in the field of conservation.

In 1962 the Outdoor Recreation Resources Review Commission reported to the President and the Congress on its plans for helping this country to provide for the outdoor recreation that more than ninety per cent of all Americans seem to want. There are many kinds of outdoor recreation, on many different kinds of land owned by cities and states and the federal government, as well as by individuals. The main problem is to provide enough of this land in places not too far from the people who want it.

The report dealt with wilderness, too. Wilderness areas, it stated, should be selected and managed "for the sole . . . purpose of maintaining their primitive characteristics."

Suppose you feel an urge to explore wild places, and you are hundreds of miles from any wilderness. What can you do? Until you can get away, let a small place do. If you are in a city, go to a park. Central Park in New York City is one of our finest examples of an area of highly valuable city land left green for the enjoyment of people. Of course, it is not wilderness.

In a little vale in a public park you may hear many birds

singing. You may find birds, too, though not so many, in a tree growing in a little patch of green beside an apartment house. On a little island off the coast, cut off from most of the civilized world, you may walk through a patch of primeval forest. Winding through a meadow behind a farmhouse there may be a brook that has tumbled down from the wooded mountainside.

Find a little wild place wherever you can. And be glad that farther away there are still wild stretches of wilderness which you may someday see.

30: The Earth and You

There is an old Hebrew story, originally from the Talmud, which goes like this:

A scholar found an old man digging a hole in the earth and asked, "At your age, must you do this heavy work yourself? Have you no sons or servants to do the work?"

The old man kept on digging and answered, "*This* I must do myself."

The scholar then asked, "But how old are you?"

"I am seventy years and seven," the old man answered.

"And what are you planting?"

"I am planting a bread tree," said the old man. "The fruits of this tree can be ground to flour and used as food for many."

"But when," asked the scholar, "will it have fruit, your tree?"

"In seventeen years and seven."

"But you will surely not live that long," said the scholar.

"No," said the old man, "I will not live that long. But I must plant this tree. When I came into this world, it was not a desolate world. I found trees and bread. I must not leave this a desolate world, but a world with trees growing. As our fathers planted, so we must plant."

We, too, can think ahead to those who will live on this earth when we are no longer here. Not all of us can plant trees. Not all of us have an acre of earth or even a backyard garden to care for. We may live far from any farm or any wilderness. But we can be aware of what the care of the soil and the wise use of all the land mean to this country and to the world. We can help other people to understand this, too.

Examples of the abuse of the land, or its neglect, are not hard to find. If you live in a city, look around you when you go to a big park. You may find a slope where only trees and a few wisps of grass are growing, with hard-packed earth around them. A tangle of bare tree roots shows that topsoil has been washed away in the rain. Little ditches run down the slope—the beginning of gullies.

Don't blame the Department of Parks too much for this erosion. They would probably control it if they could. The chances are that they haven't enough men or enough money to keep up with half the work that needs to be done in the parks. And the parks take quite a beating from the people who use them.

If you live in the country, take a look first of all at your own garden, if you have one. Pick up a handful of soil. How does it look? How does it feel? Is it dark, and crumbly in your hand?

Your garden may be a small one. Maybe it doesn't seem important to take good care of such a small amount of land. But it is. Every piece of land is important.

Look at the countryside around you. Is there a farmer who still plants his rows of corn straight up and down the slopes? You probably can't change his ways. The chances are that he thinks his corn looks just fine that way. But it might be interesting to find out what local organizations, such as your Soil Conservation District, are doing about this problem, wherever it comes up. You can spread your own knowledge of the care of the soil here and there, too, tactfully.

People in the city sometimes have unexpected opportunities to enjoy the fruits of the earth. We appreciate the shade of trees along some city streets. In New York City, people who haven't a square foot of soil to call their own can have a tree planted along the street. If you want a tree in front of your house or your apartment window, you can write to the Department of Parks for a license to plant a tree. The Department will send someone down to make sure the hole to be dug won't go through a water main, or a gas pipe or electric line. Then you will have to buy the tree from a good nursery and have their gardeners plant it. This will cost about a hundred dollars.

Not all trees will thrive in the smoggy city air, but a London plane or a gingko usually will. You will have to loosen the soil and water the tree twice a week all during its first summer.

This may not seem much like planting a bread tree. You are not even allowed to do the planting yourself. And it is fairly expensive. But you will have a tree, and maybe you will feel that you should "shout for joy and also sing." The chances are, too, that the tree will be enjoyed for a long time by many people besides yourself. People do have trees planted in New York City, sometimes more than a hundred in a year.

A city or suburban home owner with a small yard has of course a much better chance to learn how to care for the soil.

There was George Haskins, for instance. He owned a small house on a quiet street in Brooklyn, New York. In front of the house his lawn sloped gently from the house to the sidewalk. Grass wouldn't grow well there because the huge maple tree next to the street kept the soil full of its myriad big and little roots just below the surface, and the grass roots couldn't get down deep. Haskins wouldn't have parted with that tree for anything. He loved its shade in the summer. Anyway, it belonged to the city.

Haskins couldn't be bothered with planting new grass every year, so he decided to cover the whole front lawn with ivy. First he loosened the soil by digging it up and turning it over. He mixed in some rotted manure he'd gotten from the country, and compost. On top he raked in a little fertilizer. Then he cut promising pieces of ivy from the vine in his back yard, planted them about a foot apart, and watered them until the roots got started. Their smooth green leaves looked hopeful.

Meanwhile, Haskins' sloping lawn was having a small but distinct case of erosion. The soil was uncovered, except where the ivy was starting. When it rained, topsoil washed off all over the lawn and ran in muddy streams across the sidewalk, into the gutter, and down the sewer. It was gone forever, by sheet erosion. Haskins could see this happening even when he just watered the lawn with a hose. It would have been worse if the soil had not been fairly soft and absorbant, with plenty of organic matter. But it was bad enough.

This would never do. George Haskins bought some aluminum lawn edging and worked it in all around the edges of his lawn. This made a very small sort of holding wall, but it proved to be enough for all occasions except the heaviest rain. And it looked tidy. On a front lawn, Haskins had to think of that, too.

He took good care of his soil in other ways, too. He made sure he had the right kind of fertilizer. He knew that he should have plenty of organic matter in his soil, so he found a place for a compost pile in back of his garage. He built up his compost, with first a layer of plant refuse, such as leaves, grass clippings, weeds, and odds and ends of vegetables; then a light layer of lime and some fertilizer, more plant refuse, a layer of soil, and so on. The fertilizer provided nitrogen, which helped hurry up the composting process. The lime kept the decaying matter from becoming too acid and helped the bacteria along.

Every few months, Haskins turned over his compost pile, to mix it. He shoveled out some of his compost and dug it into his garden soil once or twice a year. It must be good compost, he thought, because there were such enormous healthy-looking earthworms living in it.

The garden George Haskins grew was rather wild and informal for the city, but he liked it that way. He had a corner of ferns and wild flowers from the woods. (He kept the soil for these acid and woodsy.) Annual flowers spread their seeds one year and came up here and there the next. Haskins was short of space, so some years he planted escarolle among the roses. This odd garden flourished.

If you haven't a single piece of outdoor earth where you can plant something, see what you can do indoors. Of course, a great variety of plants will grow in pots, and the earth they live in deserves better care than it usually gets.

In a glass aquarium, with a glass cover to keep it humid, you can grow your own small sample of the woods. It will probably flourish for years.

Put pebbles or coarse sand into the bottom of the aquarium (which of course becomes a terrarium), then some moist rich soil you have dug deep in a wood where you are allowed to dig. Plant, in their own woodsy soil, small plants from the woods: mosses, tiny ferns, lichens, baby evergreens, wintergreen, and such. If you are keeping small animals, too, you will need some pieces of charcoal and a supply of water for them.

The forest soil will surprise you. This is not a dead thing you have put in your terrarium. Besides the plants you intended to plant, all sorts of interesting small things will keep popping up as if out of nowhere. A long thin green stem may grow up almost overnight and then neatly uncurl a tiny fern frond at its tip. A spindly weed may wander all over and have to be cut down.

Lift the cover of your little wood first thing in the morning. Take a whiff. There is nothing like the rich moist smell of forest earth. It can take you, just for a moment, miles away.

In her novel, *An Episode of Sparrows*, Rumer Godden tells the story of a little city girl who discovers, unexpectedly, the wonder of the way seeds grow in the earth.

The little girl, Lovejoy, had stolen a packet of seeds. More than anything in the world she wanted to plant those seeds and see them grow. She lived on a poor street in London. There was no earth there at all, except in boxes. Lovejoy wanted a real garden, not one in boxes.

Her friend, Tip, said, "Under everything's dirt. Under the houses and the pavements and the road, there's dirt."

"That was true," the book goes on, "and dirt, earth, has power, an astonishing power of life, of creating and sweetening; it can take anything, a body, an old tin, decay, rust, corruption, filth, and turn it into itself, and slowly make it life, green blades of grass and weeds."

Lovejoy finally planted her seeds, in the only place where earth was open and available, a bombed place. And something came up. For three weeks after planting, Lovejoy could not get away to visit her garden. But then she did visit it and found "countless little stalks as fine as hairs, some so fine that she could scarcely see their color, others vividly showing their new green. They're *blades*, thought Lovejoy, blades of grass!" And there were little heads made of two flat leaves on a stalk—the flowers she had planted. "They must come from a sowing—my sowing," thought Lovejoy suddenly, the seeds *I* planted. . . . She knelt down . . . and very gently, with her palm, she brushed the hair blades. . . . 'It's like—earth's fur,' said Lovejoy."

Lovejoy's garden was overrun by boys and ruined, but she and Tip started again, in an abandoned church garden. She made many discoveries. She loved the fresh smell of her garden after the rain. When she got down on her knees to smell it, she made another discovery. "If you stand up the garden's little. . . . If you get right down and look along the paths, squint and screw your eyes up, it's big."

The garden was hard work. The beds in the church garden did not have enough earth, and Lovejoy and Tip hauled earth from another garden over the wall in buckets, at night. There were many complications, near tragedy, and finally a happy ending. All through the book there is Lovejoy's yearning for a garden of her own, her wonder at how things grow in the earth.

She was right to feel as she did about the earth and everything that grows in it. There is nothing more wonderful in the world.

Bibliography

Adams, Ansel, and Newhall, Nancy: *This is the American Earth*. San Francisco: The Sierra Club, 1960.

Baker, Richard St. Barbe: *Kabongo*. London: George Ronald, 1955.

Bear, Firman E.: *Earth: The Stuff of Life*. Norman: University of Oklahoma Press, 1962.

Bennett, Hugh Hammond, and Pryor, William Clayton: *This Land We Defend*. New York: Longmans, Green and Co., 1942. (Out of print.)

Brink, Wellington: *Big Hugh, the Father of Soil Conservation*. New York: Macmillan Co., 1951.

Brittain, Robert: *Let There Be Bread*. New York: Simon and Schuster, 1952.

Bromfield, Louis: *From My Experience*. New York: Harper and Bros., 1955.

——— *Malabar Farm*. New York: Harper and Bros., 1948.

——— *Out of the Earth*. New York: Harper and Bros., 1950.

——— *Pleasant Valley*. New York: Harper and Bros., 1945.

Bronson, Wilfrid S.: *Freedom and Plenty: Ours to Save*. New York: Harcourt, Brace and Co., 1953.

Brower, David, ed.: *Wilderness*. San Francisco: The Sierra Club, 1961.

249

Buchsbaum, Ralph, and Buchsbaum, Mildred: *Basic Ecology.* Pittsburgh: Boxwood Press, 1957.

Calder, Ritchie: *Men Against the Desert.* London: George Allen and Unwin, 1958.

Chandler, Alfred N.: *Land Title Origins.* New York: Robert Schalkenbach Foundation, 1945.

Chase, Stuart: *Rich Land, Poor Land.* New York: McGraw-Hill Book Co., 1936.

Clawson, Marion: *Your Land and Mine.* Pamphlet. Washington, D.C.: National Wildlife Federation, 1957.

Colby, C. B.: *Soil Savers, Work of the Soil Conservation Service of the United States Department of Agriculture.* New York: Coward McCann, 1957.

Collis, John Stewart: *The Triumph of the Tree.* New York: William Sloane Associates, 1954.

Dale, Tom, and Carter, Vernon Gill: *Topsoil and Civilization.* Norman: University of Oklahoma Press, 1955.

Early American Soil Conservationists. Pamphlet. Washington, D.C.: U.S. Department of Agriculture Miscellaneous Publication No. 449, 1959.

Epstein, Sam, and Epstein, Beryl: *All About the Desert.* New York: Random House, 1957.

Farb, Peter: *Living Earth.* New York: Harper and Bros., 1959.

Frank, Bernard, and Netboy, Anthony: *Water, Land, and People.* New York: Alfred A. Knopf, 1950.

Gerster, George: *Sahara, Desert of Destiny.* New York: Coward McCann, 1961.

Goetz, Delia: *Deserts.* New York: William Morrow and Co., 1956.

Helfman, Elizabeth S.: *Water for the World.* New York: Longmans, Green and Co., Inc. 1960.

Higbee, Edward: *The American Oasis*. New York: Alfred A. Knopf, 1957.

Hogner, Dorothy Childs: *Conservation in America*. Philadelphia: J. B. Lippincott Co., 1958.

Hyams, Edward: *Soil and Civilization*. London: Thames and Hudson, 1952.

Jacks, G. V., and Whyte, R. O.: *Vanishing Lands*. Garden City: Doubleday and Co., 1939.

Jacob, H. E.: *Six Thousand Years of Bread*. Garden City: Doubleday and Co., 1944.

Joy, Charles R.: *Desert Caravans, the Challenge of the Changing Sahara*. New York: Coward McCann, 1960.

Land, Yearbook of Agriculture 1958. Washington, D.C.: United States Department of Agriculture, 1958.

Land, Special issue of *House and Home*. August, 1960.

Lauber, Patricia: *Dust Bowl, the Story of Man on the Great Plains*. New York: Coward McCann, 1958.

Lengyel, Emil: *The Subcontinent of India*. A Scholastic World Affairs Multi-Text. New York: Scholastic Book Services, 1961.

Lord, Russell, and Lord, Kate: *Forever the Land*. New York: Harper and Bros., 1950.

National Park Wilderness, The. Booklet. Washington, D.C.: United States Department of the Interior, 1958.

Osborn, Fairfield: *Our Plundered Planet*. Boston: Little, Brown and Co., 1948.

Our Productive Land: We Can Conserve and Improve it While Using It: Agriculture Information Bulletin 106. Washington, D.C.: United States Department of Agriculture, 1959.

Our Splendid Outdoors, special issue of *Life*. Dec. 22, 1961.

Sakolski, Aaron M.: *Land Tenure and Land Taxation in*

America. New York: Robert Schalkenbach Foundation, 1957.

Sears, Paul B.: *Deserts on the March*. Norman: University of Oklahoma Press, revised edition, 1959.

Shippen, Katherine B.: *The Great Heritage*. New York: Viking Press, 1949.

Smith, Jean: *Find a Career in Conservation*. New York: G. P. Putnam's Sons, 1959.

Soil. Yearbook of Agriculture 1957. Washington, D.C.: United States Department of Agriculture, 1957.

Soil Conservation, an International Study. Rome: Food and Agricultural Organization of the United Nations, 1948.

Soil and Water Conservation. Booklet. Boy Scouts of America, Merit Badge Series, 1952.

Storer, John H.: *The Web of Life*. New York: Devin-Adair Co., 1960.

Swift, Ernest: *The Glory Trail*. Booklet. Washington, D.C.: National Wildlife Federation, 1958.

Teale, Edwin Way: "Land Forever Wild." Article, *Audubon Magazine*, May–June, 1957.

Vogt, William: *Road to Survival*. New York: William Sloane Associates, 1948.

Wilderness. Booklet, Washington, D.C.: United States Department of Agriculture, 1961.

Williams-Ellis, Amabel: *Man and the Good Earth*. New York: G.P. Putnam's Sons, 1959.

In addition to those listed, many excellent pamphlets are available from the United States Department of Agriculture. (To be ordered from the Superintendent of Documents, U.S. Government Printing Office, Washington 25, D.C.)

Index